RISK MANAGEMENT FOR THE PRACTICING PHYSICIAN

Release date: February, 1998
Initial Revision released: February, 2001
Second Revision released: May, 2004
Third Revision released: May, 2007
Fourth Revision released: September 15, 2010
Fifth Revision released: September 15, 2013
Sixth Revision released: September 15, 2016
Seventh Revision released: September 15, 2019
Expiration date: September 15, 2022

Faculty
Charles H. Mandell, MD
David B. Mandell, JD, MBA
Jason M. O'Dell, MS
Carole C. Foos, CPA

CME jointly provided by American Academy of CME, Inc.
and Guardian Publishing, LLC

RISK MANAGEMENT FOR THE PRACTICING PHYSICIAN

By Charles H. Mandell, MD, David B. Mandell, JD, MBA, Jason M. O'Dell, MS, CWM, Carole C. Foos, CPA

© 1998 2004, 2007, 2010, 2013, 2016, 2019 Guardian Publishing, LLC

Tel: 513-792-1252

This publication is designed to provide accurate and authoritative information in regard to the subject matter covered. It is available to be sold in bulk quantities to non-learners for the sole purpose of redistribution by law firms, service providers and large medical institutions with the understanding that the publisher is not engaged in rendering legal, accounting, or other professional services. If legal advice or other expert assistance is required, the service of a competent professional person should be sought.

--From a Declaration of Principles jointly adopted by a Committee of the American Bar Association and a Committee of Publishers.

The opinions expressed in this educational activity are that of the faculty and do not represent those of the American Academy of CME, Inc.

ISBN: 978-1-7340643-2-2

Manufactured in the United States of America.

METHOD OF PARTICIPATION FOR CME CREDIT

There are no fees to receive CME credit for participating in this activity. If you wish to receive continuing education credit, please do the following:

1. Review the objectives, statement of need, and disclosure information.

2. Read the activity.

3. To obtain the maximum benefit from this activity, you are encouraged to complete the self-assessment checklist at the end of each chapter, as applicable, and formulate an action plan based on each self-assessment exercise.

4. For each chapter pairing (see Credit Statement section below), go online as directed and complete the self-assessment (achieving a passing score of 70%) and the activity evaluation. If you do not achieve a passing score in three attempts, please contact CEServices@cme.com to have your account reset. Upon passing the assessment and completing the evaluation, you will be able to print or save your certificate of credit.

ACCREDITATION

JOINTLY ACCREDITED PROVIDER™
INTERPROFESSIONAL CONTINUING EDUCATION

In support of improving patient care, this activity has been planned and implemented by American Academy of CME, Inc. and Guardian Publishing. American Academy of CME, Inc. is Jointly accredited by the Accreditation Council for Continuing Medical Education (ACCME), the Accreditation Council for Pharmacy Education (ACPE), and the American Nurses Credentialing Center (ANCC), to provide continuing education for the healthcare team.

CREDIT STATEMENT

The American Academy of CME, Inc. designates each enduring material for the number of *AMA PRA Category 1 Credits*™ listed below. Physicians should claim only the credit commensurate with the extent of their participation in the activity.

Ch. 1 - The Medical Malpractice Landscape in 2019 *and* Ch. 2 - Providing Care in Today's Malpractice Environment: A Land of Diagnosis-Based Claims
Enduring material, *1.0 AMA PRA Category 1 Credit*™

Ch. 3 - When Liability Can Begin: The Doctor-Patient Relationship *and* Ch. 4 - Managing Diagnosis-Related Liability: What We Can Learn from Closed Claims
Enduring material, *1.0 AMA PRA Category 1 Credit*™

Ch. 5 - Minimizing the Risks of Miscommunication *and* Ch. 6 - Managing High-Risk Communication Areas
Enduring material, *1.0 AMA PRA Category 1 Credit*™

Ch. 7 - Managing Privacy Risks: HIPAA & Beyond *and* Ch. 8 - From Congress to Court: Results and Lessons from Recent HIPAA Litigation
Enduring material, *1.0 AMA PRA Category 1 Credit*™

Ch. 9 - Nonmedical Liability Risks for the Practicing Physician *and* Ch. 10 Risk Management Regarding Today's Technologies and Telemedicine
Enduring material, *1.0 AMA PRA Category 1 Credit*™

TARGET AUDIENCE

This educational activity is appropriate for all physicians practicing in the United States.

STATEMENT OF NEED

It is critical for physicians to provide improved patient care by fostering better communication skills with patients and staff thereby reducing the risk of patient errors that may result in liability claims. The current practice of physicians as it relates to communication with patients and practice management specific to maintain low risk for liability claims has proven to be increasing areas of challenge for medical professionals. These areas are critical to continued patient care and with improvements and implementation of appropriate management systems can mitigate risk concerns on the part of the physician if implemented appropriately. Improving risk management strategies and enhancing patient communications will result in effective information exchange between the medical team and patients.

EDUCATIONAL OBJECTIVES

After participating in this educational activity, learners should be better able to:

- Identify the principal risk factors that put physicians' practices at risk for liability claims.

- Identify common causes of malpractice/liability claims for the practicing physician, and apply effective defensive strategies.

- Apply effective strategies to avoid and/or minimize risks of liability.

- Discuss some legal issues relevant to liability concerns in a variety of practice structures.

- Use the assessment tools, recommendations and questions contained in this monograph to identify areas of risk, and formulate a strategy for corrective action.

- Apply these strategies to provide improved patient care.

DISCLOSURES

According to the disclosure policy of the Academy, all faculty, planning committee members, editors, managers and other individuals who are in a position to control content are required to disclose any relevant relationships with any commercial interests related to this activity. The existence of these interests or relationships is not viewed as implying bias or decreasing the value of the presentation. All educational materials are reviewed for fair balance, scientific objectivity and levels of evidence. Disclosures are as follows:

> Mr. David Mandell, Mr. Jason O'Dell, and Mrs. Carole Foos disclose that they are principals of Guardian Publishing.

> Dr. Charles Mandell discloses he has no financial relationships with Guardian Publishing or any other commercial company whose products or services are discussed in this material. He discloses he is a shareholder of Umedex.

> John JD Juchniewicz, MCIS, CHCP, is an employee of the American Academy of CME, Inc. He discloses he has no relevant financial relationships specific to the subject matter of this activity.

PRIVACY

For more information about the American Academy of CME, Inc. privacy policy, please access http://www.academycme.org/privacy.htm

QUESTIONS ABOUT CME CREDIT

Please contact: CEServices@academycme.org

NOTE TO LEARNERS

Please be advised that this educational activity is available in both hard copy and digital formats. Credit will only be awarded for participation in one of the formats.

About The Authors

Charles H. Mandell, MD

Dr. Mandell has a bachelor's degree from Brown University and a medical degree from Tufts University. A practicing radiologist with more than 40 years of experience, Dr. Mandell served as an assistant clinical professor of radiation medicine at Brown University.

In addition to starting a number of private practices in radiology, Dr. Mandell has served as Hospital Department Chairman, Chairman of the Human Research Committee, and Chairman of the Radiation Safety Committee.

David B. Mandell, JD, MBA

David B. Mandell is a partner in OJM Group. Mr. Mandell earned a bachelor's degree with honors from Harvard University. His law degree is from the UCLA School of Law, where he was awarded the American Jurisprudence Award for achievement in legal ethics. While at UCLA, Mr. Mandell also earned an MBA from the Anderson School.

Speaking on wealth preservation and risk management, Mr. Mandell has addressed dozens of medical societies, hospitals, and physician groups across the country. He is regularly published in medical magazines and also co-wrote *For Doctors Only: A Guide to Working Less and Building More.*

Jason M. O'Dell, MS, CWM

Jason M. O'Dell is the managing partner of OJM Group. Jason is a co-author of the book *For Doctors Only: A Guide to Working Less and Building More*, and the specialty-specific books *Wealth Protection Planning for Orthopaedic Surgeons and Sports Medicine Specialists* and *Wealth Protection Planning for Dermatologists.*

Mr. O'Dell graduated with a Bachelor of Arts degree in Economics from The Ohio State University. He earned a Master of Science degree with an emphasis in Financial Planning from the College for Financial Planning, Denver, CO.

Carole C. Foos, CPA

Carole Foos is a Certified Public Accountant (CPA) and partner in OJM Group. She has over 25 years of experience in accounting, tax planning, and financial consulting and was formerly a manger in the tax department of a Big 4 firm.

Carole is a co-author of more than a dozen financial resources, including *Wealth Management Made Simple*, *For Doctors Only* and the prior edition of *Risk Management for the Practicing Physician*. She has also authored numerous articles and presented lectures, webcasts, and podcasts on tax planning, wealth management, and other financial topics.

Ms. Foos earned a Bachelor of Science in Business Administration from Xavier University, where she majored in accounting.

Table of Contents

INTRODUCTION:
CAN WE DO THE RIGHT THING?

As a physician, it is no longer so simple to follow the adage "do the right thing" as it was in the past. When a physician began a general medical practice in the 1930s, the "right thing" meant taking care of the patient with the limited tools at hand, compassion and skill. While doing so, there was the absolute assurance from patients and society that the doctor was in charge.

For a physician of this era (as was the case for our fathers and grandfathers), the family home often doubled as the medical office. A pantry could be the examining room, a dining room the office, and an open front hall and parlor the waiting room. Office hours could be afternoons and evenings, with house calls and hospital visits in between. Moreover, there would be little, if any, office overhead; no receptionists, nurses, clerks or even billing services. In those times, the doctor was truly a "one-person show" (and, almost exclusively at that time, a "one-man show").

The pharmacologic armamentarium of the time consisted of aspirin, phenobarbital, sulfur, zinc and boric acid ointments, digitalis, mercury compounds, and a few others. The major tools battling disease were hope, faith, and the doctor's will. To the generation of the 1930s, 1940s, and early 1950s, the phrase "the will to live" was more than a slogan. Rather, it was a recurring reality in the battle with infectious disease. And it was the physician who was up front in that battle, holding high the flag of hope and knowledge.

We know that, for most of you, this is the image you still hold of yourself and most of your colleagues. And you should. Medicine is still a noble calling, and the best of us give of ourselves to our patients as we continue the fight against disease.

Why then is this monograph necessary? Why, if we are trying to do our best for our patients, are we attacked for the relatively few serious mistakes we do make? The answers to these questions are complex and will be examined in some detail later. Yet, behind these questions is the implicit assumption that we are on the right side of the battle. We are fighting the forces of disease and debilitation. We are trying to make people feel better and have more active and pain-free lives. However, physicians are no longer the only ones involved in this noble fight.

Today, the federal government, state governments, and insurers want to be seen as leading the fight against disease. Accountable care organizations (ACOs) have emerged as another standard-bearer and regulatory necessary in this fight. Health systems, large group clinics, and even medical school clinical faculties may want to seize the battle flag from us. Consumer groups and employers also want to lead our populace to "healthy living" if for an altruistic goal or simply to reduce costs. Is it any surprise that the individual patients are unclear as to which flag to follow? Is it any surprise that some of us no longer seem to know which flag is leading in the right direction?

As confusing as this fight has become, we must remember that disease and ill health are still the enemy, not the other flag-bearers. Our obligation is first and foremost to our patients to improve their lives. The insurers and public policy groups cannot, and should not, distract us from this primary responsibility.

It is often easy to become distracted from our priorities when we are besieged by the countless nuisances that sidetrack us in daily practice. Most prevalent of these are pervasive government regulations and the changing requirements of insurers and ACOs. In addition, the distraction of malpractice and other liability risks also looms. Whether distractions come in the form of an increase in the number of insurance forms, the practice of defensive medicine, or drug company marketing to patients, our attention is constantly being diverted from of our professional goal of serving patients.

Written jointly by a practicing radiologist with more than 40 years of experience, an asset protection and risk management attorney, a financial consultant, and a CPA, this monograph will address the principal threats that put your practice at risk for lawsuits – malpractice and others. Further, we will suggest ways to strengthen and protect you, so that you can securely and confidently keep your purpose— improved patient care—in sharp focus.

Once you understand the dangers that surround you, and learn effective strategies for avoiding and minimizing them, you will be better able to provide improved patient care. In this way, you will be able to more effectively "do the right thing" for each of your patients.

CHAPTER 1

The Medical Malpractice Landscape in 2019

Since our previous edition of this monograph in 2016, the medical malpractice landscape has been fairly steady. Attempts to impose state government controls on malpractice lawsuits has had some limited success, although the federal initiatives have stalled. Let's examine the latest malpractice data and then discuss the efforts to curb non-economic damages.

- The latest data on malpractice liability

The following data comes from National Practitioner Data Bank (NPDB), a computer database of the U.S. Department of Health & Human Services, in their 2019 report, which analyzes data up through 2018.[1]

1. In 2018, malpractice payouts across the United States totaled $4.031 billion, an increase of 2.91 percent from 2017.

2. Medical errors related to diagnoses continued to lead the allegations of malpractice. This claim represented 34.1 percent of all payouts in 2018.

4. The three leading areas of claims from 2018 payouts were:

- Diagnosis-related 34.1%

- Surgery-related 21.4%

- Treatment-related 21.1%

As we discussed in earlier editions of this monograph, diagnosis-related claims continue to be a focus for the malpractice bar. Also, recall from earlier editions that malpractice cases often settle – often for undisclosed amounts. These cases take five years on average to "settle," and during that time, attorneys' fees have continued to climb. In fact, these fees have climbed well in excess of the increase in patient payments. Not only are plaintiffs' attorneys benefiting from protracted litigation, but defense attorneys for you and your insurance company have also seen a significant increase in their fees for each case. Insurance companies traditionally have delayed payments in any type of claim for as long as possible, so they could continue to collect premiums and earn interest on their money. So, they too have been part of the long delay in case settlement. It appears, however, that these companies' out-of-pocket costs may be increasing faster than their earnings and they too are now complaining. The insurance companies finally may be on the side of the physician in wanting faster resolution of these cases.

Caps on Non-Economic Damages

One of the leading debates and areas of legislation in the last decade concerns the implementation of caps on non-economic damages in medical malpractice cases. In these types of cases, "non-economic damages" essentially mean payments for "pain and suffering." Determining the amount of non-economic damages is traditionally subject to broad discretion by juries, who try to equate pain and suffering to money – which is virtually impossible to do fairly and consistently.

Advocates of caps on such damages have argued that, without them, jury awards are inconsistent and unpredictable – forcing insurers to counter this uncertainty by charging higher premiums. Further, they argue that such unpredictability creates a major obstacle to out-of-court settlements, thus increasing litigation and the overall legal costs in the system.

Opponents to such caps argue that they penalize the plaintiffs who will endure the most pain and suffering. "By forever freezing compensation at today's levels, caps discriminate against a single class of Americans whose members are destined to suffer a lifetime of depravation of dignity and independence."[2]

Do Caps Work?

There is now over a decade of experience with non-economic damage caps on malpractice payouts. The states that have tort reform laws showed about equal numbers above and below the median malpractice costs for physicians. This suggests that tort reform has little influence on malpractice premium costs.

In fact, a 2014 study by the National Institutes of Health (NIH) "found noneconomic damage caps reduced payments by $42,980 (15 percent; p<0.001), with a $250,000 cap reducing average payments by $59,331 (20 percent; p<0.001), while a $500,000 cap had no significant effect. Effects varied according to specialty and were largest in specialties with high average payments, such as pediatrics. This suggests that the effect of noneconomic damage caps differs by specialty, and only more restrictive caps result in lower average payments."[3]

Older data that we referenced in early editions from the American Medical Association has shown that there may be some marginal effect in keeping physicians in a state, or attracting them to a state, when that state enacts cap legislation. According to a 2005 study published in the Journal of the American Medical Association (JAMA), the adoption of direct medical malpractice reforms that limit the size of awards led to a greater growth in the overall supply of physicians. Three years after adoption of reforms, the study found that the physician supply increased by 3.3 percent. According to the study, the direct reforms had a larger effect on: (1) The supply of non-group vs. group physicians; (2) The supply of most specialties with high malpractice insurance premiums; and (3) States with high levels of managed care.[4]

Conclusion

Malpractice liability has held fairly steadily over the last three years and the cost of malpractice is increasingly becoming a smaller portion of practice expense, except in the case of obstetrics and a few surgical specialties.

What has changed in the past three years and is most affecting physicians is the entry of 10,000 new patients a day to Medicare rolls, and the pressure on Medicare to reduce physician fees to keep up with patient demand and a relatively fixed Medicare budget. We will not delve into this issue here, but recognize that this financial stress can greatly contribute to the stress that any added liability brings to your practice. We hope, in some small way, that this monograph will help you, the physician, not only practically – to reduce the risk of a medical error or liability event – but also psychologically – to help ease the stress that the present crisis may create for you in your own practice.

Chapter 1- References

1. Anjelica Cappellino, "Medical Malpractice Payout Report for 2018", www.theexpertinstitute.com, April 23, 2019.

2. Perlman, Peter. "Don't Punish the Injured," *American Bar Association Journal* (May 1986).

3. Seabury, Seth A., Helland, Eric & Jena, Anupam. "Medical Malpractice Reform: Noneconomic Damages Caps Reduced Payments 15 Percent, With Varied Effects By Specialty" See http://www.ncbi.nlm.nih.gov/pmc/articles/PMC4278571/ .

4. Kessler, Daniel. "Impact of Malpractice Reforms on the Supply of Physicians," *Journal of the American Medical Association (JAMA) June 1, 2005—Vol 293, No. 21.*

Providing Care in Today's Malpractice Environment: A Land of Diagnosis-Based Claims

The malpractice landscape in the United States today has held relatively steady over the past few years as the opening chapter showed. Nonetheless, diagnosis-based claims are still the most prevalent in the payouts.

Perhaps even more significant than these statistics has been the shift from lawsuits arising in the hospital arena to those originating from outpatient situations over the past decade or more. Not only have a wider cross-section of physicians been involved, but, the burden for payment has increasingly been transferred to the individual physician rather than the hospital. As more physicians become hospital employees, the payment burden may shift back again, but this time it may be the physician's salary and work habits that are squeezed rather than his/her personal insurance costs.

In this chapter, we again examine the changing medical malpractice landscape. Specifically, we discuss how medical treatment has shifted to an outpatient scenario, how malpractice claims increasingly involve diagnosis-based claims, and how a fast-service mentality has put more time pressure on the practicing physician. Finally, we suggest ways to alleviate the time pressure in practice, which should lead to improved patient care and reduced malpractice risks by providing you with more time to diagnose, discuss, and document.

The Shift to Outpatient Treatment

Over the past 20 years there has been a continued shift toward outpatient medicine.

There are many reasons for this shift, but most can be separated into what we call either "push" or "pull" factors. Push factors are those pushing patients out of the traditional hospital setting, and pull factors are those pulling patients into outpatient clinics or offices.

Push Factors

The push to move patients out of the hospital and into the clinic or private office environment began with the advent of capitated payments to the hospitals in the form of Medicare diagnostic-related groups (DRGs). This early form of capitation initiated single global payments to hospitals for a single admission. Therefore, the faster patients were seen in hospitals, and the less that was done to them, the larger the potential hospital profit.

There has been a substantial decrease in hospital days per patient admission under these rules. With the advent of managed care, the pressure to decrease length of stay has been even more intense and the rise of for-profit hospitals has also furthered this trend. Average length of hospital stay is under 3.5 days. State-mandated minimum length-of-stay for procedures such as normal birth and delivery and mastectomy have been instituted. The public, not the hospitals, have demanded this. This is a trend that we expect will continue.

Only recently has the impact of this push to shortened hospital stays been felt in the area of patient litigation. Patients and their families often resent this push outward to home or nursing facilities. For the physician, this resentment may result in a lawsuit, particularly if the patient, in retrospect, had been sent home too early. Complications of early discharge, particularly in the elderly, often propel patients to the physician's office or to the emergency department, sometimes only hours after discharge. The physician is then in the position of having to either fight for readmission or manage the patient outside of the hospital. The potential for a liability suit in these circumstances is particularly high. In 2016, Medicare has announced penalties for hospital re-admissions within 30 days of discharge if related to the same condition. This may ease the pressure on early discharge, as hospitals will now get penalized financially for the first time. This may help doctors, but it is too early to tell.

Increasingly, physicians are becoming hospital employees or contractors and bound by hospital guidelines. For private practice physicians this may be a mixed blessing. They can follow hospital guidelines and hope for protection from such lawsuits, but they will frequently be shut out of hospital visits altogether. For the diminishing number of physicians with "true" private practices, hospital-related liability will probably decrease, but not as much as hospital-related income.

Risk managers in hospitals, health systems and ACOs too often look at their entity's financial risk of longer stays rather than the physician's risk of assuming care for a too-sick patient outside the facility. Thus, the private physician may begin to see sicker patients in their practice or in the nursing home. The decision to discharge the patient will not be yours, but you will be responsible for them after discharge. This could be a recipe for outpatient disaster, but it probably will be beyond your control. In most states, out-patient malpractice claims have increased significantly, and it is likely this will continue as managed care grows. When we discuss managed-care liability issues, you will see how this "push outward" results in a higher exposure for the physician.

Pull Factors

At the same time that hospitals and insurers are "pushing patients out of hospitals," there are aggressive groups "pulling patients into outpatient care." Those doing the "pulling" often have stronger motive to attract patients than traditional nonprofit hospitals have had.

The "pull" for patients today often comes from the for-profit sector, frequently from large, well-financed organizations. Twenty years ago, outpatient surgical centers pioneered this revolution. Often, these were started by local physicians who saw an opportunity to lower costs for their patients, secure more convenient operating room schedules for themselves, and make a small profit at the same time.

Gradually, these small, independent "surgicenters" were purchased by national companies seeking to establish a niche in the medical economy. The ability of these companies to pull patients out of hospital operating rooms with physician incentives became significant. Although these independent companies operated with little outpatient competition for a period, hospitals eventually realized that they could "compete against themselves" by setting up a for-profit division to handle the outpatient surgery. Hospitals frequently became part of a bigger corporation that had both for-profit and nonprofit arms.

Initially, only low-risk procedures were performed in these outpatient surgery centers. Over the past 10 years, however, more and more major procedures have been moved to these locations. Although this move does not always correlate with increased outpatient liability, it is a major contributing factor. In one study, treatment-related and surgery-related claims constituted 43 percent of all outpatient claims.[1] OB/GYN and general surgery are most often. The percentage of litigation attributable to procedures in surgery has been decreasing in the 1990s. Although the reasons for this are not definitely proved, we have some observations that may be helpful.

The Shift to Diagnosis-Related Claims

Like the infectious organism that constantly changes and adapts to antibiotics and other drugs, the law of malpractice liability has been changing over the past 30 years. As malpractice defense lawyers constructed solid defenses to certain types of claims (particularly, failure to receive informed consent), plaintiffs' lawyers created new claims and found new sources of liability (most prevalent: diagnostic liability).

Over the past decade, partly as a consequence of increasing outpatient surgery, physicians and hospitals have focused their risk management on protecting against claims of failure to receive informed consent. Legal counsel eventually showed both doctors and hospitals how to successfully defend against these claims by telling the patient what surgery procedure he or she is going to have; what the benefit, complications, alternatives, and risks are; and documenting these conversations. Through the procedures and forms now accepted as standard practice, the physician transfers much of the malpractice risk to patients and their families. As long as the patient and family are competent to understand the conversation and the consent form, witnesses, and documentation are solid, a physician's defense barrier will be difficult to overcome despite an unfavorable result.

In this way, much of medical risk management in the 1980s focused on the informed consent issue, tightening up the forms, increasing the documentation, and requiring relatives to be present to sign. But lawyers are flexible, as is the law. If they could not overcome tight consent forms, they could look for theories of liability for which consent was not a key issue. Their most popular theory of liability is failure to diagnose.

Consent, in failure-to-diagnose cases, is almost irrelevant. Who would consent to one's physician failing to find out what is wrong with him? What would a defensive consent form look like? Perhaps something like this:

"As your doctor, I will use my best efforts to discover what is wrong with you. I do not know what tests I will order or what they will show. I do not know whether or not I will find the cause of what is bothering you or just a lot of other things wrong with your chemistry or anatomy that do not bother you. I do not know if what I will find will be significant in the long or short run.

If I do find something to treat, I will try to find the medicine that will not make you sick or give you a worse reaction than the problem that you came in with. I will give you only such medicine as your insurer will allow. And if I cannot order the right test or refer you to a specialist because of your insurer's restrictions, I will try to handle your problem as best I can.

But because I am doing my best, you agree to all the above conditions and agree not to sue me, my office, and employees, even if we mess up."

Obviously, patients would not sign this form.

Until this point, physicians' defense attorneys have not been able to design a solid defense to diagnosis-based claims by using a standard informed consent form. However, some state legislatures have begun to protect physicians by instituting preapproved standards of practice. If physicians follow these guidelines, they may have an effective defense when bad outcomes occur. These statutes have not yet been tested extensively through cases, so it is too early to tell whether this defensive positioning will be successful. This trend, which a few years ago seemed to be growing, is now at a standstill. Guidelines to protect you in private practice are still few and far between.

Because an effective defense to diagnosis-based claims has not yet emerged, the number of claims continues to rise. Part of the reason behind this increase is that patients are being encouraged by the media to assign more liability to their doctors for diagnosis. Recent articles have advised patients to have the doctor document to them in writing the reason that a particular test is not necessary. Whether you think it is not necessary or the payor thinks it is not necessary or too expensive, you put yourself in a tenuous legal position by signing such a document.

The end to this shifting pattern of litigation is not in sight. As long as it makes financial sense to do so, attorneys will continue to file lawsuits against physicians, especially those practicing in the most vulnerable areas. For the moment, it appears that diagnostic-related claims will be the main vehicle for liability. Within the broad heading of diagnosis-based claims are three theories of liability: (1) failure to diagnose; (2) delay in diagnosis; and (3) misdiagnosis. Each of these lends itself to litigation in many areas, but some general comments may help to further analyze the risk.

We are still seeing the same types of claims to be most prevalent: failure to diagnose, delay in diagnosis, and misdiagnosis. The entire spectrum of diagnostic-related claims seems to be a temporal one, with the three types of claims listed above as part of one continuum. Consider the following case study, which illustrates how these claims are interrelated.

Case Study

When first seen by a physician at the ER, an elderly woman who we will call Mrs. Johnson presents complaining of a fall outside her apartment. The emergency room physician who examines her quickly may diagnose her as having a hip fracture or bruise.

Here, if no x-ray films are ordered, the result may be a misdiagnosis of a soft-tissue injury alone. Alternatively, it may simply be an early case of delay of diagnosis if the fracture becomes clinically apparent one week later. It may even become a failure to diagnose if the occult fracture leads to a severe arthritis requiring a hip prosthesis months to years later. The basic facts for the patient's visit are the same.

The type of liability may not be revealed until the lawsuit is filed. Further, under many courts' rules, the plaintiff's attorneys need not choose any theory of liability when beginning the lawsuit, or even at trial. Thus, they might allege all three theories of liability and let the jury decide which one "fits the bill." As any observer of jury trials will confirm, juries may find for the plaintiff even when none of the claims are proved, only when certain elements of different claims are shown. This only makes a successful defense to diagnosis-based claim even more difficult.

Recommendation

From your common knowledge, conversations with colleagues, and professional periodicals, make a list of common misdiagnoses in your specialty/practice. Do the same for failures to diagnose and delays in diagnosis. By preparing and analyzing this list, you will better understand your vulnerability to the risks of diagnosis-based claims. Simply by becoming more aware of these liability sources, you are likely to put an increased importance on diagnosis and be less likely to rush to diagnosis.

The Pressure to Diagnose Quickly

To accurately understand today's malpractice liability environment, one must also consider how the time continuum is working against physicians today. Increasingly, the public has become accustomed to what we will call the "McDonald's mentality of service:" an expectation of standardized and very fast service. This mentality has slowly but steadily moved out of the traditional service industries and now has changed expectations of medical service for the outpatient setting or in-hospital stay. For the physician, this means that we are expected to heal our patients in less and less time: a time pressure that has made it more difficult for us to diagnose disease by observing its natural history.

The trend of pushing patients out of hospitals also allows for less diagnostic time and shorter intervals of clinical observation. Many hospitals require all diagnostic studies to be completed within 12 to 24 hours after being ordered, and many institutions strongly encourage testing to begin as soon as the patient is admitted. The critical pathways that hospitals create to streamline the work-up allows little time for "nature to take its course."

Since traditional medicine has used the progression of signs and symptoms to help diagnose disease, many physicians, particularly internists and general surgeons, have given up one of their most valuable tools in dealing with sick patients. Diagnostic testing is rapidly replacing diagnostic observation. Patients, hospitals, and insurers are all pushing physicians into quick diagnoses and quick diagnoses lead to a higher risk of misdiagnoses.

Unfortunately, the same pressures exist in the outpatient clinic or office setting. With office overhead rising, per-patient reimbursement falling, and new restrictions on testing and referrals, there is less time and less information with which to make accurate diagnoses. And this rapid spiral shows no sign of slowing. Again, misdiagnoses or failures to diagnose become increasingly common. Consider the following real-life case of an ordinary failure to diagnose. It demonstrates the danger of rushing to diagnose, which often prevents the physician from considering the most serious cause of symptoms. This oversight can have significant liability consequences.

Case Study

Mrs. Stern was a 50-year-old teacher in good health. On her first visit to the internist in May, she complained of some slight rectal bleeding but no other acute symptoms. The physician performed a quick rectal exam and found some internal hemorrhoids. He assured her that the bleeding was from the hemorrhoids, and sent her home on iron supplements.

The patient returned to the doctor's office in July. She still had rectal bleeding but her anemia was no worse. Her doctor looked quickly at her laboratory results, saw no change, and recommended she continue with the iron. As his schedule was extremely tight, the physician moved on to the next patient. Over the next 3 months she experienced increasing fatigue. But when she spoke to the office nurse, she was told that the doctor was busy and that he would call her back. He never did.

When Mrs. Stern returned to the doctor in October, the physician realized that she was sicker than he had initially thought. He decided to admit her for further testing. A barium enema examination revealed a sigmoid mass. Surgery was uneventful, but she died six months later.

The case study of Mrs. Stern shows one subtle type of rush to diagnose. Rather than a blatant case study that involves a failure of the busy physician to listen to the patient initially, this case illustrates how even a good doctor, with a justifiable initial diagnosis, can be rushed into sticking to that diagnosis when further symptoms should lead him/her to investigate other possibilities. In this case, the malpractice was not the initial visit, but the follow-up visit, when the doctor failed to take the time to initiate a further workup.

Diagnosis-related claims may be different problems in different settings. In the busy office practice, delays may be compounded by the failure to get patients back to the office in a timely fashion or to notify them of the results promptly enough. Often this speed is out of the primary-care physician's control. Delays in getting results back from laboratories or specialists' reports mean delays in accurate diagnoses. This, in turn, means an increased risk of liability.

Recommendation

Give yourself more time by building a strong electronic communications system in your office. A top-notch electronic communications system can eliminate, or at least ameliorate, many of the potential hazards of this "rush to diagnose" age. Before specific recommendations are suggested, ask yourself whether you have adequate communications infrastructure to move data in and out of your office or whether the communication itself produces a delay in diagnosis. Any delay due to the electronic communications system increases the risk of liability to a diagnosis-based claim. Much time can be saved over a month or year simply by implementing an efficient, effective system. With the use of electronic medical records and internet-based communication tools, this should be possible at a progressively reasonable cost.

An efficient electronic communications system improves the quality of a practitioner's care not only because the physician and staff are less rushed, but also because the office is better able to meet patients' expectations for fast service. For example, the 45-year-old woman with a mammogram at noon on Friday might expect a report that afternoon. A weekend delay for her may be too long. A two-week wait for a mammogram appointment may be reasonable for some but not for the woman who just found a lump in her breast. The greater the publicity surrounding the disease (such as breast cancer), the greater the pressure for rapid and accurate diagnosis. Patient satisfaction may be as tied to the timing of medical care as it is to the quality of that care.

Consider the following case study of a gynecologist, whose office recently instituted an updated communications system.

Case Study

Initially, some of his staff and patients complained about the new communications system Dr. Dee established in his office. Now, all patients and staff unanimously praise it. Staff members spend less time on menial activities (giving directions to the office asking the same questions of each patient), and patients are able to interact with the office efficiently, so they can get the information they want quicker.

For example, the voicemail system has options for callers who want prescriptions refilled (they must have all pertinent information ready to record), need directions to the office, want billing questions answered, and even a hook to Dr. Dee's phone line. Of course, callers can always press "0" to speak to a staff member, and there is an emergency option prompt at the outset of the message. Also, the office is able to make good on its promise to respond to every message within 24 hours on workdays.

This system has received positive feedback from patients and staff members. Between improved efficiency of the staff and better patient relations, this system easily justifies its monthly rental cost.

This case study briefly demonstrates one example of how a communications system can improve patient care and free a physician and his staff from the incessant time pressures that exist today.

Depending on the structure of your practice and your area of practice, a communication system may have different options. Consider the following recommendations in implementing an up dated communications strategy in your practice:

- Hire a communications consultant for your office. Perhaps your major insurers have such a program. If you are in primary care, the managed care organization wants you and needs you. They have the resources to analyze and improve your practice management. And they should do this at their expense. If you can lower your practice overhead, you can provide care at lower costs and make you and the HMO more financially stable.

- Check with your hospital or the laboratories where your testing is done. They are the beneficiaries of your referrals. Ask them to set up a secure email system to send you reports and make sure there are safeguards of privacy and proper patient assignment integrated into this system.

- Consider a patient-friendly, voice message system that may send you email or text alerts. As the above case study demonstrated, such a system can free staff members to work on more meaningful duties and can improve patient satisfaction. See the telemedicine chapter for more on using technology to reduce risk.

- Take a personal course on computer skills, particularly word processing and email. Not only will you be leading your office by example, but your improved efficiency will reduce the business pressures on your time.

- Remember to consider the issue of patient confidentiality when information and report transfer options are concerned. Be sure that everything in your office is in a secure location, removed from the gaze of patients' prying eyes. If email becomes the preferred mode of information transfer, make sure passwords are used to limit access to confidential information.

Chapter 2:
Self-Assessment Checklist

The following are common signs that a physician may be susceptible to making a quick diagnosis. Use this checklist to evaluate your own behavior and as a preventative reminder to slow down and make more thorough analysis before diagnosing or staying with a diagnosis.

1. Do you spend a decreasing amount of time listening to patients, failing to obtain critical information and an increasing amount of time entering information into the patient's electronic health record?

2. Do you spend less time in a physical examination of patients and therefore miss key signs?

3. Do you rely too often on "playing the odds" for the most common diagnosis?

4. Do you rule out the worst or most severe diagnosis without proper justification rather than considering all the alternatives?

5. Do you order only the routine tests and fail to consider less usual possibilities?

6. Do you take only a new patient's history related to the specific complaints of the visit rather than his/her full medical history?

7. Have you contacted your referral specialists to create a rapid and established method of receiving their reports?

8. Do you have a voice-message system at your office? For each each physician, NP and PA in your practice?

9. Do you get your outside lab reports faxed, mailed, or e-mailed to you?

10. Do you dictate your notes or write them down? How long does it take for your staff to transcribe the dictated notes?

11. Have you considered voice recognition software to transcribe notes?

12. Ask outside physicians who try to speak with you on the phone: "How long does it take to get me on the phone?" Perhaps you need additional phone lines.

13. Ask new patients who want to schedule an appointment: "How long does it take to get the staff member on the phone?" or existing patients who are awaiting reports: "How long does it take to get the staff member on the phone?" Perhaps a voice message can route these calls more efficiently.

No matter what time pressures you are under, never fail to do the following:

- Thoroughly examine the patient.

- Take and document a thorough history.

- Conduct those diagnostic tests and procedures generally considered appropriate and those that rule out the most serious diagnoses.

- Carefully eliminate alternative modes of diagnosis and treatment.

- Set up an efficient communication system, particularly for patient follow-up.

Chapter 2- References

1. National Practitioner Data Bank, 2006 Annual Report, U.S Department of Health & Human Services, p 26.

Method of Participation for Obtaining CME Credit for Chapters 1 and 2

There are no fees to receive CME credit for participating in this activity. If you wish to receive continuing education credit, please do the following:

1. Review the objectives, statement of need, and disclosure information.

2. Read the indicated chapters.

3. To obtain the maximum benefit from this activity, you are encouraged to complete the self-assessment checklist at the end of each chapter, as applicable, and formulate an action plan based on each self-assessment exercise.

4. Go online using the URL below and complete the self-assessment (achieving a passing score of 70 percent) and the activity evaluation. If you do not achieve a passing score in three attempts, please contact CEServices@cme.com to have your account reset. Upon passing the assessment and completing the evaluation, you will be able to print or save your certificate of credit

www.academycme.org/actID=19GU161
activity code: 19GU161

When Liability Can Begin: The Doctor-Patient Relationship

The establishment of a doctor-patient relationship and malpractice liability are intimately related. Unfortunately, the establishment of the doctor-patient relationship is much less formal than one would expect. Most of us are conditioned to believe that this relationship starts when the doctor sees the patient in a formal consultation or another in-office situation. The courts, however, have not always followed such a narrow definition. Under the law in this area, a written contract or other documentation between the parties is not a prerequisite to the doctor-patient relationship. In fact, the patient need not have ever visited the doctor's office, or even spoken with the doctor, for the relationship to begin and for a standard of care to be imposed.

In this chapter, we will examine the most common ways an informal doctor-patient relationship is established and how to avoid these liability-creating scenarios. We will also discuss a risky area of the relationship once it has been established: the physician's duty of confidentiality. Finally, we will provide case studies to demonstrate real-life situations in which clinicians are put at risk because of these issues.

Informal Social Setting

The first type of doctor-patient relationship that we should consider is that which has been established in an informal social setting. One ordinarily does not think of casual advice given to an acquaintance or a friend as establishing the doctor-patient relationship. In most cases, this is not a problem. However, let us take the example of the acquaintance:

Case Study

Al, a friend of one of your golfing friends, tells you about some mild back pain while you are both out on the golf course. You suggest that this is probably due to minor muscle strain and that Al should come see you in the office on Monday morning.

In the interim, however, Al becomes sicker, and his wife urges him to go to the emergency room. Having spoken with you, Al feels reassured and tells his wife that there is no need to do so. When conditions worsen, however, he ultimately winds up in the emergency room with an acute myocardial infarction, which has progressed to the point at which serious complications ensue. Although he had never sought formal consultation from you, Al may have relied upon your advice that this was only a mild muscle strain. Relying on your advice, a reasonable thing to do under the circumstances, Al chose not to visit the hospital earlier.

If Al can show that a doctor-patient relationship existed by your conversation, the law will measure your actions against a reasonable standard of care: what other physicians in your medical community would have done under similar circumstances. As physician experts can always be found to say you did not do enough—that is, make the diagnosis that Al might have risked having a myocardial infarction, that Al should have gone to the emergency room, that Al should have called you later that day—you could easily be held liable in this situation.

What can we learn from Al's case study? First, even the most innocuous conversations in informal settings can be interpreted by patients in ways that actually reduce the quality of the medical care given to them. Moreover, these seemingly innocent conversations can create liability. Further, as a potential target, the physician should always consider the liability ramifications of even casual advice. If you are going to give medical advice, you should expect to be held accountable for that advice, no matter how informal the situation and no matter how the patient acts on that advice.

Recommendation

Whenever possible, avoid giving medical advice in informal settings. Recommend that people see you in the office (or at home) before you make a diagnosis or advise any course of treatment. If informal advice is given, make sure that the patient is followed up promptly with an office or hospital visit.

Telephone/Texting/Emailing/ Social Media Advice

In the chapters on miscommunication and on managed-care risks, we will analyze the dangers of telephone advice and we will cover texting/emailing/social media in the chapter on telemedicine. Nonetheless, it is important to discuss here because it is often a means of creating the doctor-patient relationship. Perhaps even more common than the conversation with an acquaintance in a social setting is the situation in which a friend, colleague, or family member calls for medical advice. Many of these people are not, in fact, our patients before the phone conversation. This may not be true after the call. In short, the doctor-patient relationship can be established over the telephone. The same may be said for an email or through texting or social media.

The most dangerous element of creating a doctor-patient relationship through any electronic means is that you have deprived yourself of the opportunity to see the patient in person and to examine him/her. Therefore, it is much more likely that suggestions that you make will turn out to be erroneous. It is not uncommon in these situations to make a diagnosis or recommendation over the phone that you never would have made in person, had you had the opportunity for a physical examination.

Recommendation

Avoid giving medical advice to potential patients over the phone or through electronic means per above. Recommend that they see you in the office (or at home) before you make a diagnosis or advise any course of treatment. If you must give a telephone consultation: Document, Document, Document! As you're not seeing the patient in person, you are relying on their description, not your own observation. Write "the patient says she has no back pain" rather than "there is no back pain."

Payment and Place Not Controlling

Unlike ordinary contracts, the existence of the doctor-patient relationship is not dependent upon "consideration" (charging of a fee). Money (or anything else of value) need not change hands for the relationship to be established. Whether or not the patient pays you, either through insurance or directly, is irrelevant to your relationship with him. All patients have the same rights to your services and to the same standard of care, regardless of payment.

It is not necessary to actually see or talk with the patient for the doctor-patient relationship to be established. If, for instance, you are on vacation and have hired a substitute to cover for you, you may be liable for the acts of your substitute. The law will imply the relationship between you and the patient through your substitute, who has become your agent for medical services.

Self-Assessment

How do you hire substitutes now? Is there any formal record-keeping for the hiring process?

Recommendations

When you agree to hire someone to replace you, make sure that the replacement has the same level of medical competence that you have. Document your search for a competent replacement and the qualifications process, if any. Keep copies of your correspondence with the substitute(s) and their resume(s) and curricula vitae.

Recognize that because the substitute is new to your patients, there may be more distrust and the doctor-patient relationship, and the medical treatment itself, may suffer as a result. It is important, therefore, that you instruct anyone covering for you on those areas that you consider to be of high risk such as potential emergencies or referrals.

New Court Case Allows Liability Even Where No Doctor-Patient Relationship Existed

As we complete this seventh edition of our monograph in 2019, we followed the development of a possible landmark case in the junction of medical malpractice risk and the physician-patient relationship. In a case decided by the Minnesota Supreme Court – and, thus, only the law of the land in that state of this writing – the court held that the existence of a physician-patient relationship was not a prerequisite for a medical malpractice action.[1]

The case of Warren v. Dinter arises out of the care provided to a woman (Susan Warren), who complained of abdominal pain, fever, chills, and other symptoms to a nurse practitioner at a health clinic. After testing showed that Warren had an elevated white blood cell count, the nurse practitioner suspected infection and sought hospitalization for her, calling the hospital. The nurse practitioner's call was randomly assigned to a hospitalist to discuss admission.

After a brief conversation, during which the physician was unable to view the patient's medical record, the physician and the nurse practitioner discussed hospitalization and whether the elevated white-cell count and blood sugar could be the result of diabetes. The physician did not recommend hospitalization during the conversation and the nurse practitioner did not seek hospitalization for the patient following the conversation. The patient subsequently died from sepsis caused by an untreated staph infection. Warren's family sued both the nurse practitioner and the physician for medical malpractice.

The district court granted summary judgment on the issue of duty, concluding that the relationship between the patient and the hospitalist did not create a doctor-patient relationship. The court of appeals affirmed. The Minnesota Supreme Court reversed these decisions, allowing a case to go forward against the physician. The court noted that a physician-patient relationship is not a necessary element of a claim for professional negligence, holding that (1) a physician owes a duty of care to a third party when the physician acts in a professional capacity and it is reasonably foreseeable that the third party will rely on the physician's acts and be harmed by a breach of the standard of care; and (2) it was reasonably foreseeable that the patient in this case would rely on the hospitalist's acts and be harmed by a breach of the standard of care.

Before this ruling, Minnesota law generally required the existence of a physician-patient relationship to sustain a malpractice action against a physician. The Court's decision to rely on a broader legal theory of "foreseeability" represents a troubling change that may expose physicians and other health professionals to malpractice risk in a variety of actions that were previously protected, including unbilled consultations.[2] While this case only controls in the state of Minnesota, it does represent a legal trend to expand the scope of potential physician liability.

Patient Confidentiality

One aspect of the physician-patient relationship that can cause a great number of problems is patient confidentiality. You must be absolutely certain that, in the physical layout of your office, the patient's medical and financial information is not accessible to other patients and staff who are not involved in the patient's care Doing a reasonable job to minimize disclosure of confidential information is not enough. You must prevent such disclosures absolutely or risk liability. We will discuss HIPAA privacy issues specifically in two chapters later in the monograph.

You also must be certain that, in the information transfer involved in billing, a patient's confidential information is not mistakenly disclosed to individuals or companies that have no legal right to obtain it. A written release form is necessary for you to give any of this information to a third party. Make sure you use it. Often, insurance companies and lawyers will attempt to gain confidential information through telephone calls to your staff. Unscrupulous collection agencies may even call your office asking for information on patients under the guise of medical insurance.

Recommendations
Train your staff to deflect all questions that relate to a patient's confidential financial or medical information. Instruct all staff that

such information should never be made available without previous written authorization from the patient.

If you use an outside billing service, make sure that they follow the same guidelines. Just because they are not your direct employees does not mean that you will not be liable for their indiscretions.

Chapter 3:
Self-Assessment Checklist

Assess your physical office set-up for patient confidentiality. Get out a diagram of your office or clinic premises and re-identify the individual points of patient interaction. If no such diagram exists, create one, using the following guidelines:

1. Where do new patients sit for initial data interviews? Does only one person collect the information? Is it visible to other office staff? What about to other patients? Do you have clear glass partitions? Would one-way glass be preferable? If you have older patients, is there room for an accompanying spouse or child to sit?

2. Are our areas of confidential information gathering soundproof? Sit outside the area yourself and have your staff role-play as patient and clerk. Can you hear their conversation? If you can, make sure you correct the problem.

3. Are patient exam rooms visually protected and soundproof? Can patients or staff see or hear you? Do not trust thin walls to block all conversations. An overheard conversation can embarrass patients and create liability if the patient's identity is revealed when he/she leaves the room.

4. Do you have the type of practice in which your patients do not want their names known to others under any circumstances (certain plastic surgery practices, clinics where sexually transmitted diseases are tested, etc.). If so, how do you call these patients into your office or examination room. Consider an impersonal or coded system upon check- in, so names or initials are not used. Even a local area beeper system for each patient may be cost effective and very private.

5. To test these issues in your practice, consider asking a close friend or colleague to pose as a patient in your office: spend time in your waiting room, examination room, corridors. They will be able to give you an unbiased view of your office and staff currently handling these concerns. Just be careful not to distress your staff during such a "test."

Chapter 3 – References

1. Warren v. Dinter, 2019 No. A17-0555 WL 1646469 *1 (Minn., April 17, 2019).

2. https://www.mnmed.org/news-and-publications/News/ MN-Supreme-Court-Rules-Physician-Patient-Relations? utm_source=Informz+Email&utm_medium=Informz& utm_campaign=Informz+Emails&_zs=7CPLX&_zl= kE8b1

This space is provided for the purpose of creating a diagram of your office/ clinic space using the guidelines on the preceding pages.

Managing Diagnosis-Related Liability: What We Can Learn from Closed Claims

Analysis of closed claims data provides one of our most reliable tools in predicting future malpractice risks. We can survey not only the types of cases accounting for the current malpractice epidemic, but we can also predict future trends. An in-depth analysis allows us to probe the reasons behind many lawsuits, to profile a typical plaintiff and defendant, and to analyze the type of situations that lead to litigation.

The Physician Insurers Association of America (PIAA) continues to provide a great service in this analysis. This association of dozens of national and local malpractice insurers provides detailed reports in specific areas. With combined coverage of more than 100,000 physicians, their statistics are large enough to be meaningful and they have developed excellent survey and reporting techniques. By using their recent studies as an example, we will see how this type of data can help us understand the risks involved in individual medical practices.

In this chapter, we will examine the results of three large PIAA studies: claims involving breast cancer and myocardial infarctions. In addition, studies of lung and colon cancer claims will be briefly analyzed. Here, we maintain our analysis of the same studies reviewed in the prior version of the monograph, as there have not been studies since that impact our conclusions materially.

Liability Factors and Causes – More of the Same

In this 2019 edition of our monograph, diagnostic-related claims continued to be the largest single root cause of professional medical liability claims. In this regard, nothing has changed from our last few editions. In fact, in a 2018 study conducted by Boston-based insurance provider Coverys (from data collected in 2013-2017), diagnosis-related claims accounted for 33% of claims and 47% of all indemnity payments.[1] Interesting key findings from the report are that the majority of claims still result from outpatient or office visits, with more than half of diagnostic related cases related to testing, either ordering, performing, interpreting, or communicating results. In this atmosphere, testing for cancer continues to be a major source of liability risk.

Breast Cancer: Lessons From PIAA Studies

The PIAA breast cancer surveys are useful to examine because, in a number of cases, this area now constitutes the largest single category of malpractice claims. The dollar total of these claims is second only to obstetric and delivery-related cases. Furthermore, many physicians have contact with patients with breast cancer, and many groups of physicians are involved in the lawsuit analysis. We also have the advantage of four surveys: 1990, 1995, 2002, and recently 2013. These surveys demonstrate changes in trends in the malpractice landscape.

The first and most obvious trend in malpractice related to breast cancer (as noted in earlier chapters) has been the shift from claims involving surgery or procedures to diagnosis-based claims. Whether the claim was failure in diagnosis, misdiagnosis, or delay in diagnosis, this category of claims continues to climb. We have already examined some of the reasons for this trend.

The important thing to acknowledge here is that the diagnostic claims can involve many, if not all, types of generalists and specialists, much more so than surgery- or procedure-oriented claims. In the mammography studies, the categories most often involved were radiologists and primary care physicians. Gynecologists, surgeons, pathologists and oncologists were also involved. In a limited number of cases, hospitals and larger entities were affected.

As physicians, we may have over-sold ourselves to the public, creating the impression that we can easily diagnose and cure breast cancer before we have developed the tools to accurately diagnose the disease consistently at an early stage. Given this scenario, it is easy to see why so many malpractice cases related to breast-cancer diagnosis have surfaced. If the public believes that we can find this disease and cure it easily, they will become angry when we do not. And with tens of thousands of deaths annually, their anger is easily understood. If we are not going to admit our shortcomings in the ability to diagnose breast cancer early, we can expect the number of lawsuits to increase. Add to this the tendency to call even a biopsy with a few abnormal cells "cancer", and the scare elicited by the word is enough to provoke even the most rational patient to become agitated and look for a scapegoat in the process.

If every patient with the possibility of getting breast cancer were referred for annual mammographic screening, we might expect that the radiologist reading these mammograms would be the dominant lawsuit target. Yet, the most recent study, the Physicians Insurers Association of America 2013 Breast Cancer Study, showed that although radiologists were the number-one defendant group, they accounted for only 43 percent total of physicians named in lawsuits.[2] This was up from 33 percent in the 2002 study.[3] But what of the other groups?

Family doctors and internists who had previously accounted for 8 percent of all physicians involved in lawsuits in 2002,[4] increased to 16 percent in the 2013 study.[5] Obstetricians and gynecologists fell from 23 percent in 2002[6] to 16 percent in 2013.[7] Surgical specialists remained about the same at 12 percent, as did all other doctors at 13 percent.[8]

The leading cause of lawsuits in the 2013 study was clearly one related to mammography, which the PIAA calculated was a central part of 35 percent of all claims.[9] Other leading factors included a missed manual examination and operative procedures of the breast.[10]

The above causes appear to be fairly straightforward failures of either knowledge or communication. We have to ask why this occurs. It may be because there is a widespread belief that breast cancer is asymptomatic until very late in its course and that, in younger premenopausal woman, the disease is relatively uncommon. Such beliefs appear to be widely held among all physician groups. In fact, reviewing these cases, we can see the growth of lawsuits reflecting our continuing education process in understanding this disease.

In prior studies, the PIAA had done a careful interview study of the women who had filed lawsuits.[11] They found that, indeed, many cancers were not asymptomatic. In fact, although a painless mass was recorded as the most common symptom in 46 percent of the cases, painful or tender breasts (with or without a mass) was the patient's reason for presentation. If, as the treating physician, you assume the pain is due to a cyst, you will be correct the majority of the time, especially for younger patients. However, a significant minority of the time (25 percent) you will be wrong. If so, you will face a tragic situation in terms of the patient's health and possibly significant legal liability. To provide better care for your patient and to avoid malpractice liability, follow these important recommendations.

Recommendations

When a patient presents with any complaints referable to the breast, even at a relatively young age, consider the worst possible diagnosis: cancer. Unless you are absolutely familiar with the complete and actual history and symptoms of the disease, DO NOT EXCLUDE YOUR MOST SERIOUS DIAGNOSIS ON HISTORY ALONE. This could be a serious mistake.

The PIAA study noted above also demonstrates that breast cancer is not uncommon, even in young premenopausal women. Do not assume that, because you do not hear much about a common disease in a young or older age group, it does not occur. This attitude can be extremely dangerous. In the most recent study, most of the lawsuits were filed by women under 50 years of age.[12] In fact, the younger the woman, the higher the individual case settlement value.

Do not dismiss diagnosis simply because the patient is in a "low-risk" age group. Consider the following case study as a reminder:

Case Study

Carol was an active tennis player, aged 34 years. With some intermittent back pain, she visited her internist's office. Her symptoms were not severe and responded to analgesics and an exercise program. While at the doctor's office for her next six-month visit, Carol mentioned to the doctor the slight, but definite, pulling pain she had been experiencing in the left breast. Physical examination revealed a lumpy breast, and the doctor told her he was sure it was cystic disease, which she had experienced before.

At her next appointment six months later, Carol again mentioned the breast pain. The physical exam had not changed. Carol had thought very little about the discomfort although it was present most of the time. Again, her physician reassured her that he felt that this was cystic disease of the breast and she should not worry about it.

One morning, she thought she felt a new lump in that breast. She was due for her annual gynecologic examination three weeks later and pointed the lump out to the gynecologist at the visit. Despite what she felt was a normal physical examination, the gynecologist ordered a baseline mammogram. A finely calcified small mass measuring about 1.5 centimeters was discovered. The patient underwent excisional biopsy, laser lumpectomy and radiation. Despite what seemed to be adequate treatment, she died two years later. Carol's estate successfully sued the internist, alleging delay in diagnosis leading to death.

Here, Carol's internist was in a difficult situation. Although he found a lumpy breast upon physical examination, because of her young age, he did not feel it necessary to rule out breast cancer with any type of further study on the first visit. Statistically, this course of action seemed reasonable. However, when she again presented with symptoms of breast pain, the wisest course of action would have been to ignore the statistics (which would point against breast cancer) and rule out the most serious diagnosis leading from the patient's complaints. Here, that most serious diagnosis would have been breast cancer.

Risk Assessment and Screening Guidelines

An important question for the clinician to ask is "Can you trust national society recommendations when it comes to screening this common disease?" This is a question which is receiving increasing scrutiny as both government-sponsored task forces and NGOs (non-government organizations) give their opinions. Today the American Cancer Society, which not too long ago opposed screening women under age 50, now strongly recommends annual mammographic screening in the 40- to 50-year-old age group. Yet, a government-sponsored and well respected task force recommended biennial screening at age 50.[13]

Even radiologists are admitting that the emphasis on early screening for stage 1 and stage 2 cancers has NOT affected the number of patients getting advanced breast cancer (stages 3 and 4).

Assessing risk profiles can be aided by studies such as those of the PIAA. Per above, the average patient suing for breast-related diagnosis is a young (under 50) and often healthy woman. Unlike the plaintiffs of 15 years ago, who sued almost exclusively because of complications of treatment, today's patients frequently sue because of failed expectations in diagnosis or the inadequate physician response to their complaints.

Often, the disgruntled patient is most upset that the physician did not recognize the early symptoms that presaged the severity of the disease, no matter how innocuous the symptoms appeared at the time. This is especially dangerous for the clinician with cases in which minor symptoms could be caused by a host of both major and minor diseases. By relying too heavily on statistics and odds, you may fail to rule out the most serious pathology.

For example, every day in emergency rooms physicians see the "mild mid-back pain patient" who returns two or three times. The most common diagnosis is that the patient is suffering from muscular skeletal pain. However, the patient may eventually demonstrate a dissecting aortic aneurysm. Such a missed diagnosis can lead to tremendous liability.

A slight right lower quadrant pain and low-grade fever in an older patient may increase in severity over a few days, turning out to be a ruptured appendix with peritonitis. There is no easy solution to the problem of diagnosis-related lawsuits.

To ensure the highest level of patient care and maximal

avoidance of liability, you must follow the recommendation to always consider and rule out the most serious diagnosis.

Myocardial Infarctions: Lessons From Leading Studies

Failure to promptly diagnose and treat myocardial infarction is a common mishap in medical practice and is a frequent allegation in medical malpractice lawsuits. Thus, it is valuable to be able to analyze closed claims studies of this type of lawsuit.

1. Seminal PIAA Study

The PIAA myocardial infarction study from 1996 is the leading study in this area. This study involved 349 paid cases, in which 495 physicians had payments made on their behalf.[14] In slightly more than half of the cases involving diagnosis-based claims, the patient presented in the provider's office, whereas in one third of these cases, the first contact with the patient was in the ER. In terms of specialties, family physicians were sued most frequently, with cardiologists surprisingly the fifth most common defendant group. See below:

Physician Group	No. of Payments
Family/General Practice	160
Internal Medicine	109
Emergency Medicine	75
Cardiology	34
Other Specialties	35
Surgical Specialty	9
Physician Extenders	4
Corporation	2
Hospital	57
Total	495

This study pointed out the fallacy that risk analysis for myocardial infarctions should be calculated only by age and history. Although high incidence of risk factors was present among those who suffered myocardial infarctions (44 percent had hypertension, 43 percent smoked, and 22 percent suffered from hypercholesterolemia), al-most 70 percent of the group had no previous history of coronary artery disease, and 83 percent had no previous myocardial infarction. Further, 47 percent of claimants were under the age of 50.[15]

The overall average payment in myocardial infarction cases was around $300,000, but for the 30- to 39- year-old patient age group, it averaged $470,000, confirming that much of settlement amounts in these cases are replacement of lost wages, which are higher for younger patients. (These numbers are gleaned from cases that, overwhelmingly, are settled before any trial phase).[16]

Perhaps the most revealing aspect of the PIAA study is the data on the diagnoses involved in the cases. Continuing with the trend we mentioned in Chapter 1, in this study, pure diagnosis-based claims (195) clearly outnumbered both therapeutic-based claims (45) and claims involving both diagnostic and therapeutic errors (109).[17]

Although pain was the most common complaint of patients in the myocardial infarction study (83 percent of all patients reported pain as the initial symptom), what was most interesting was the physician's initial impressions of these cases. In 26 percent of the cases, the doctors diagnosed the pain to be of the gastrointestinal origin or (in 20.7 percent of cases) of muscle origin.[18]

These initial impressions may help to explain why, in 65 of the cases, no diagnostic studies were ordered and, in 170, no electro-cardiograms. Common tests performed were cardiac enzymes (60), chest radiographs (58), other laboratory tests (29), and stress tests (16). In essence, the physicians involved in these cases failed to consider the most serious diagnosis and rule it out by testing it.[19]

Providers' Initial Impressions in Cases with Misdiagnosis:[20]

MI	2.6%
CAD	4.6%
Anxiety	5.3%
Respiratory DX	6.3%
Angina	6.9%
Other	13.2%
Cardiac Etiology	14.5%
Musculoskeletal	20.7%
Gastrointestinal	26.0%

Nonetheless, ordering the proper test is not the end of liability risk factors. It must be interpreted accurately. In the PIAA study, failure to properly interpret the test or failure to get the results promptly were a liability factor in 57 percent of cases in which an electrocardiogram was ordered.[21] Lack of expertise and failure of communication continue to be problems.

The PIAA study on myocardial infarction stands as a powerful illustration that, in order to enhance patient care and limit liability, clinicians must maintain a high suspicion for coronary artery disease, regardless of whether the patient presents in-office or in an emergency room, and even if the patient does not fit the typical high-risk profile.

2. Doctors Company Study of Cardiology Claims

In this analysis of claims involving only cardiologists, 429 closed claims from 2007 to 2013 were analyzed.[22] Similar to the PIAA study, diagnosis-based claims lead the list – failure to diagnose was alleged in 25 of the closed cases. Next most common were lawsuits stemming from procedural or surgical complications and fifth most common were claims related to medications.[23]

2019 Impressions

In 2019, the situation for failure to diagnose is arguably much worse for the physician than it was 20 years ago (when compared to the PIAA study) and even worse than the more recent Doctors Company study. A large component of liability today can be failure to provide lifesaving treatments that were not available at the time of the original study and that have even improved from the last decade.

Many hospitals have interventional cardiologists available 24/7 to perform angioplasty as a lifesaving procedure. More cardiac surgeons are available in smaller communities. The costs of failing to promptly diagnose an acute infarct have risen because of the increasing availability of emergency treatment, where delay of even a few hours can alter the outcome. As physicians, we have become the victims of medicine's successes, if we fail to immediately make the correct diagnosis or referral.

Recommendations

Do not be misled by "traditional" low risk factors such as youth, lack of a history of heart disease, or gender. Many members of these low-risk groups suffered myocardial infarctions and became claimants in this study. As we mentioned earlier, always consider the most serious diagnosis when patients present with symptoms that could possibly be related to myocardial infarction, then rule it out through testing.

Specific Recommendations From
PIAA Myocardial Infarction Study

- Document all patient complaints relative to pain/pressure and its location.

- Document any family history of heart disease and all personal history of heart disease including complete risk factor profiles.

- Request and document the results of any previous evaluative cardiac studies and compare the results of any present studies to the previous studies.

- Follow any patient presenting with any symptoms indicative of a heart condition until the diagnosis is ruled out, even if diagnostic testing is inconclusive and even if the patient is relatively young.

- If clinical suspicion is present, despite unchanged or negative electrocardiogram, recommend an exercise tolerance test.

- Have the same index of suspicion for the patient who presents in the office as for the one who presents in an emergency department.

- Promptly report any positive test findings to the referring physician, and follow up with other physician consultants regarding tests, etc.

- Create a handout using the points below in italics, as recommended by the PIAA, to your patients. This will educate patients about the seriousness of myocardial infarction and will improve communication between the patient and you, allowing you to make more accurate diagnoses.

As a patient, you can assist your clinicians in making a timely diagnosis and providing the correct treatment.

- Take the possibility of a heart attack seriously, even if you first see your doctor in his or her office.

- Discuss any family or personal history of heart disease.

- Mention any pain and pressure and its location.

- Cooperate with your clinician to continue pursuing a complete diagnosis if you have symptoms that could indicate a heart attack such as pain or pressure in the chest area and shortness of breath. Do not assume it is just a gastrointestinal problem or a respiratory ailment, even if the initial tests are inconclusive.

- Do not rule out the possibility of a heart attack just because you are young, especially if you have risk factors such as smoking, hypertension, high blood pressure, obesity, or a family history of heart trouble.

- Assist your clinician in securing copies of any previous studies done to evaluate heart disease.

Recommendations From the Doctors Company Study

In the article describing this study from the American College of Cardiologists, recommendations included:

1. Be more aware of the most prevalent types of diagnosis or procedural errors

2. Engage in meticulous informed consent

3. Pay close attention to documentation, workup and follow up after complications.[24]

Aortic, Lung and Colon Cancer Studies

Four older but seminal studies by PIAA—one in 1991 on colon cancer and two on lung cancer (1992, 2004) and a 2010 study on Aortic Aneurysm — also demonstrate the increasing prevalence of diagnosis-based claims.[25, 26, 27, 28] Further, these studies show that clinicians cannot simply rule out a cancer diagnosis simply by relying on the classic risk factors such as age and family history.

In all four studies, a failure or delay in diagnosis were significant reasons leading to claims. In the colon cancer study, failure to diagnose or delay in diagnosis were most often due to failure to refer for endoscopic or barium examination (79 percent). Failure to respond to the patient's complaint (19 percent) and failure to check for questionable bleeding (15 percent) were also significant factors. Failure to refer to a specialist was a factor in 15 percent of the cases.[29]

In the original 1992 lung cancer study, delay in diagnosis was due to inadequate evaluation (60 percent) and/or failure to respond to an abnormal x-ray film report (44 percent). Failure to communicate was claimed in 20 percent of the cases.[30] In the most recent study of 2004, however, these numbers had reversed. Inadequate evaluation dropped to 20 percent of causes, but failure to communicate results to the patient satisfactorily rose to 50 percent![31]

In the aortic study, failure to consider a diagnosis of aortic dissection was a major cause of lawsuits. Another cause was failure to ask for surgical consultation once a diagnosis had been established.[32]

Lessons

What can we learn from all of these studies as a whole? First, we would urge you to obtain your own copies of these studies, available at $200 each from the PIAA. Beyond this, we see some common lessons from which every clinician can benefit.

The worst or most serious diagnosis is the one you do not want to overlook

Even if you consider the serious problem unlikely, you should put it under the "rule-out" category and document all other negative supporting data. In both the breast cancer and myocardial infarction studies, failure to diagnose because of a patient's young age or atypical symptoms lead to poor outcomes and physician liability. The old adage "plan for the worst, hope for the best" is very true in diagnosis liability.

Diagnostic related claims are not going to decrease. They represent the leading theory of liability for clinicians in almost all specialties. Be prepared. If there are approved practice guidelines in your area, follow them. If your patient population is high risk because of age, social, or economic factors, calculate that into your planning. This is one area in which a good defense is critical.

Recommendations

More specific recommendations include the following:

1. Beware of the patient who seems too young to have the disease. Is it our own fear of mortality or our wish that these diseases only occur at the end of life that causes us to overlook cancer and heart disease in the under-50 age group?

2. Pain and bleeding, although ubiquitous, are often serious symptoms. Consider the most serious diagnosis and rule it out.

3. If you are not sure, refer!!! This gets harder under managed care, but so is missing diagnoses in unfamiliar areas.

4. If you do not thoroughly understand all the presenting symptoms and clinical course of a disease, learn them quickly, and rule out serious disease or refer.

5. If you have ordered diagnostic testing, understand their accuracy limits. Have a system to record and follow up results. Communicate results to your patient. COMMUNICATE!!!

6. Defensive thinking and behavior are not necessarily bad for your patients. Failure to think of the worst diagnosis, failure to rule it out with appropriate testing, and failure to diagnose treatable disease are bad for your patients. In fact, it is best not to think of this behavior as "defensive medicine" but rather as "good medicine." The goal is to provide the best diagnostic care for your patients.

Chapter 4:
Self-Assessment Checklist

- Might you see cases of breast cancer, myocardial infarction, lung or colon cancer in your practice?

- Do you usually disregard breast cancer as a diagnosis in premenopausal women because of their age?

- When diagnosing female patients presenting with pain (but no lump) in their breasts, do you typically assume the pain is due to a cyst? If so, you might make the same mistake as Carol's internist did in her case study.

- Does your diagnosis of myocardial infarction rely heavily on the classic risk factors: age, weight, whether or not the patient smokes, and family history of heart problems?

- When treating patients presenting with symptoms possibly relating to myocardial infarction, do you typically have the same index of suspicion for individuals presenting in the office as for patients presenting in the emergency department?

- When treating patients presenting with symptoms possibly relating to myocardial infarction, do you typically document all patient complaints relative to pain/pressure and its location?

- When treating patients presenting with symptoms possibly relating to myocardial infarction, do you typically document persona and family history of heart disease?

- When treating patients presenting with symptoms possibly relating to myocardial infarction, do you typically document the results of previous cardiac studies and compare them with any studies you have ordered?

- When treating patients presenting with symptoms possibly relating to myocardial infarction, do you typically continue diagnostic testing (including a stress test) until the diagnosis is ruled out?

- When treating patients presenting with symptoms possibly relating to colon cancer, do you typically refer for an endoscopic or barium examination?

- If the examples in this chapter do not relate to your specialty, what are the "high risk" conditions in your specialty? How are you managing your diagnosis-related risks with regard to these conditions.

Chapter 4 – References

1. https://www.claimsjournal.com/news/national/2018/03/15/283628.htm

2. Physicians Insurers Association of America. Breast Cancer Study: Rockville, Md: November 2013.

3. Physicians Insurers Association of America. Breast Cancer Study: 3rd Edition. Rockville, Md: 2002.

4. Physicians Insurers Association of America. Breast Cancer Study: 3rd Edition. Rockville, Md: 2002.

5. Physicians Insurers Association of America. Breast Cancer Study: Rockville, Md: November 2013.

6. Physicians Insurers Association of America. Breast Cancer Study: 3rd Edition. Rockville, Md: 2002.

7. Physicians Insurers Association of America. Breast Cancer Study: Rockville, Md: November 2013.

8. Physicians Insurers Association of America. Breast Cancer Study: Rockville, Md: November 2013.

9. Physicians Insurers Association of America. Breast Cancer Study: Rockville, Md: November 2013.

10. Physicians Insurers Association of America. Breast Cancer Study: Rockville, Md: November 2013.

11. Physicians Insurers Association of America. Breast Cancer Study. Rockville, Md: March 1990.

12. Physicians Insurers Association of America. Breast Cancer Study: Rockville, Md: November 2013.

13. See http://www.uspreventiveservicestaskforce.org/Page/Document/UpdateSummaryFinal/breast-cancer-screening.

14. Physicians Insurers Association of America. Acute Myocardial Infarction Study. Rockville, Md: May 1996.

15. Physicians Insurers Association of America. Acute Myocardial Infarction Study. Rockville, Md: May 1996.

16. Physicians Insurers Association of America. Acute Myocardial Infarction Study. Rockville, Md: May 1996.

17. Physicians Insurers Association of America. Acute Myocardial Infarction Study. Rockville, Md: May 1996.

18. Physicians Insurers Association of America. Acute Myocardial Infarction Study. Rockville, Md: May 1996.

19. Physicians Insurers Association of America. Acute Myocardial Infarction Study. Rockville, Md: May 1996.

20. Physicians Insurers Association of America. Acute Myocardial Infarction Study. Rockville, Md: May 1996.

21. Physicians Insurers Association of America. Acute Myocardial Infarction Study. Rockville, Md: May 1996.

22. "Avoiding Lawsuits: Understanding Cardiology Malpractice Claims." American College of Cardiology. February 15, 2015.

23. "Avoiding Lawsuits: Understanding Cardiology Malpractice Claims." American College of Cardiology. February 15, 2015.

24. "Avoiding Lawsuits: Understanding Cardiology Malpractice Claims." American College of Cardiology. February 15, 2015.

25. Physicians Insurers Association of America. Colon Cancer Study. Rockville, Md: 1991.

26. Physicians Insurers Association of America. Lung Cancer Study. Rockville, Md: 1992.

27. Physicians Insurers Association of America. Lung Cancer Study. Rockville, Md: 2004.

28. Physicians Insurers Association of America. Aortic Disease Claims Study. Rockville, Md: 2010.

29. Physicians Insurers Association of America. Colon Cancer Study. Rockville, Md: 1991.

30. Physicians Insurers Association of America. Lung Cancer Studies. Rockville, Md: 1992; 2004.

31. Physicians Insurers Association of America. Lung Cancer Studies. Rockville, Md: 1992; 2004.

32. Physicians Insurers Association of America. Aortic Disease Claims Study. Rockville, Md: 2010.

Method of Participation for Obtaining CME Credit for Chapters 3 and 4

There are no fees to receive CME credit for participating in this activity. If you wish to receive continuing education credit, please do the following:

1. Review the objectives, statement of need, and disclosure information.

2. Read the indicated chapters.

3. To obtain the maximum benefit from this activity, you are encouraged to complete the self-assessment checklist at the end of each chapter, as applicable, and formulate an action plan based on each self-assessment exercise.

4. Go online using the URL below and complete the self-assessment (achieving a passing score of 70 percent) and the activity evaluation. If you do not achieve a passing score in three attempts, please contact CEServices@cme.com to have your account reset. Upon passing the assessment and completing the evaluation, you will be able to print or save your certificate of credit.

www.academycme.org/actID=19GU162
activity code: 19GU162

Minimizing The Risks of Miscommunication

In the chapter on diagnostic risk management, we discussed how reduced in patient stays and shortened office visits have impeded the physician's ability to use the traditional technique of observing the disease process over time to aid in diagnosis. This change has altered the physician's approach to diagnosis over the last ten years in that diagnostic tests have been substituted for diagnostic observation. In a parallel shift during the last decade, significant changes have also occurred in the area of physician communication.

In this chapter, we will examine the shifts in physician-patient communication and how those shifts have created new risks, threatening the quality of patient care and creating additional malpractice dangers. We will also examine other important communication risks in practice, including those related to informed consent, communications with a patient's family, or even with other physicians. Throughout, we will provide recommendations for managing these risks, in an attempt to improve patient care and keep liability low.

Traditional Doctor-Patient Communication

Traditional societies, such as western European, have viewed medicine as a somewhat magical process. The physician-healer was in possession of this magical knowledge that he dispensed in small doses to each patient. The traditional images of the strong, silent American hero fed the image of the physician "taking care of his patients." In this quasi-parental role, the physician was not expected to, nor did he feel the need to, explain his actions to patients.

His charts were his property, not the patients'. His prescriptions, often written in Latin, preserved the secret magical code between physician and pharmacist. The physician healer was indeed "captain of the ship," responsible to no one except his conscience.

In this atmosphere, patients had little choice but to put their faith in physicians. "Faith," like "magic," implied a passive role for the patient, while the doctor battled with the forces of disease. Indeed, the patient was discouraged from asking questions, and rare was the physician who felt he had to explain his actions, even in cases with disastrous outcomes.

As recently as 30 years ago, in a tradition going back thousands of years, communication was unidirectional from patient to doctor. The carefully obtained and documented patient history was the backbone of diagnosis. Disease was to be sought out by looking for its natural course in the minutely documented history of the patient. In an era before computerized tomography (CT) scans, ultrasounds, magnetic resonance imaging (MRI), and endoscopies, the view inside the patient's body was through the patient's history.

Two major trends in the 1970s changed this perception of patient communication. The first trend diminished the importance of patient history, and the second trend challenged the passive role of the patient.

The Shift in Doctor-Patient Communication

In 1974, the development of the CT scan changed the approach to diagnosis. Although nuclear medicine had already been scanning patients for almost 10 years, it was CT scanning and the resultant publicity that convinced doctors and patients that, at last, we could see inside the human body relatively easily. No longer would patients and physicians have to observe the natural history of disease. They could look for disease directly. CT and ultrasound scanning opened almost all of the body to direct view.

Autopsies as the answer to disease became passé. And, in some ways, so did the patient's history and its accompanying physical examination. The hands-on magical touch of the physician, which for thousands of years had reassured patients, had begun to diminish. Machines began to replace the hands, ears, and eyes of the physician.

The second major shift of the 70s was the emergence of a class of patients who felt they had not fared well under the traditional system and were ready to revolt. Women of all ages gathered together in support groups and discussed their bodies, among other things. *Our Body, Ourselves*, a seminal self-help book for women published in Massachusetts, became the *Uncle Tom's Cabin* of the women's medical revolution.

Women challenged the notion that only physicians had the right to medical knowledge. Disenfranchised from the medical profession for centuries, they saw in their feminism a way to communicate knowledge to each other outside traditional medicine. They requested, indeed often demanded, to learn more from their doctors. No longer content to play a passive role in society, they refused to play a passive role in the doctor's office. As women demanded more information, their husbands and boyfriends did also. The magic of one-way physician communication had begun to evaporate.

If those of you who are under 45 think that this history presentation is too dramatic, ask your older colleagues about women in medicine before this revolution. There were few women in medical school before 1970, and many residency programs openly refused to take women. Taking away the one-way communication became an effective move for women wishing to introduce equality into the medical establishment.

The New Era of Doctor-Patient Communication

What is the impact of these two shifts 45 years later? Clearly, there has been a loss of some of the physician mystique that one-way communication fostered. Older physicians, of course, will have more trouble adjusting to this than younger ones, for whom this type of magic probably never existed.

One group of physicians may have particular trouble with this issue: physicians born and trained in other countries. These doctors, who trained with more classical traditions, may find American patients "too pushy." If you come from this type of training, you may need to constantly fight the tendency to treat your patients in the traditional one-way communication mode. Such interaction will only frustrate American patients today, and, although you may not be able to discern it, this frustration will lead to lower levels of patient satisfaction with their medical care. On the other hand, younger U.S.-trained physicians will likely have less frustration operating in a two-directional communication environment. However, these physicians may not know how to use the mystique of one-way communication to their advantage; specifically, when dealing with patients who have immigrated from another country.

These patients, especially in large urban areas, have never experienced the communication revolution, and still expect their physicians to make all their decisions for them. "Whatever you say," is a common response as is, "You are the doctor." However, there are as many communication risks when encountering a passive patient as there are for more openly difficult patients. We will discuss communication risks generally in the next sections, leaving discussion on more difficult patients for the next chapter.

Managing Communication Risks

In today's medical environment, dominated by the patient's expectation of a two-way communication mode, there are more ways to miscommunicate than ever before. Ineffective communication with patients can lead to misdiagnoses, patient frustration, and even malpractice lawsuits.

Miscommunication with other physicians can also lead to delays and omissions in care, which also may bring liability. We will discuss physician-patient communication first and then address physician-physician communication.

Physician-Patient Communication

Communication between a physician and patients (or their families) is, by far, the leading communication problem in risk management. In fact, recent studies of all malpractice risks have demonstrated that communication breakdowns are the number-one factor leading to litigation, even more than a substandard result. Good communication is great medicine and greater risk management.

A classic study of 120 physician offices in Oregon and Colorado, demonstrated how important physician-patient communication is to quality patient care and how communication errors can lead to malpractice lawsuits.[1] The study, which analyzed communication behaviors of primary care physicians and surgeons, separated physicians into "no claims" doctors (those with fewer than two malpractice claims filed against them) and "claims" doctors (those with more than two claims against them). Significant differences in communication behaviors of "no-claims" and "claims" physicians were identified in primary care physicians, but not in surgeons.[2]

Compared with "claims" physicians, "no-claims" primary care physicians used more statements of orientation (educating patients about what to expect and the flow of a visit), laughed and used humor more, and tended to use more facilitation (soliciting patients' opinions, checking understanding, and encouraging patients to talk). "No-claims" physicians also spent more time on average in routine visits than did "claims" physicians (mean: 18.3 versus 15 minutes).[3]

Recommendations

1. At the outset of a patient examination, use orientating statements that help the patient develop appropriate expectations about the visit. "First I'll examine you and then we will talk the problem over" or "I will leave time for your questions" are both helpful.

2. During the examination, use facilitative comments to extract more and better information from the patient. Statements like "Go on, tell more about that" or opinion solicitors like "What do you think caused that to happen?" are extremely useful.

3. Do not assume that the same communication skills are appropriate for every specialty group.

In the above study, there was an insignificant difference between "claims" and "no-claims" surgeons. In your specialty literature, find out more about what types of communication skills are beneficial for your practice.

Assessing the Patient

The first critical step in managing communication risk with your patient is to assess your patient's psychosocial background and expected response. This is crucial if you are to avoid the common pitfalls leading to strained doctor-patient relationships and even liability. Although this assessment will be a challenge regardless of the patient's age or background, it is especially difficult with foreign-born patients who speak little or no English.

For example, the Southeast Asian immigrant patient may be unlikely to ask you many questions. Your main challenge in this case will be getting enough of an adequate history to even begin your workup. Not only will language be a problem, but the traditions of eastern medicine are so different from traditional western approaches that even when the patient understands your English, you may be "speaking a different language." Consider the following case study:

Case Study

Minh, a 37-year-old Southeast Asian man, entered the emergency room with a classic presentation of RLQ pain, fever, and leukocytosis. In taking the history, the hospital personnel asked Minh if he had recently eaten. The patient misunderstood the question, saying "no" to what he thought was the question of whether he wanted something to eat. Exploratory surgery was begun one hour later. Unfortunately, not only was a normal appendix found, but the patient aspirated during recovery, and developed a difficult-to-treat aspiration pneumonia. The surgeon, anesthesiologist, and hospital were all sued and were found liable for initiating surgery without adequate history and precautions to prevent aspiration.

This case demonstrates the absolute necessity of being able to have a meaningful two-way communication in order to glean an accurate patient history. What could the physicians here have done differently? The most obvious answer is to have an interpreter available who can translate the hospital team's questions and the patient's responses. Best is a professional interpreter who also understands cultural nuances that may prevent the patient from accurately giving a history. Second best is a staff member or patient family member who can act an intermediary interpreter. The family member option, while typically free and easier to arrange, can have numerous drawbacks – from the patient not being forthright in front of the family member (as they would with a professional interpreter) to the family member not being truly fluent in English and thus missing key pieces of information in the translation.

Other Issues and Recommendations

What kind of language do you use in your practice? If it is the language of medical consultation, the patient or their family may not understand you. And if they do not, any adverse outcome of this lack of understanding may result in malpractice. This may be as easily proved as is the lack of informed consent. Especially when you are giving follow-up instructions, be sure you know and document what the patient understands.

If you work with bilingual or non-English speaking patients, have routine follow-up orders or instructions printed in the patient's language. The consultant report to the referring physician should be in English, but the letter to the patient should be in his or her first language if not English. Your consent forms in office or hospital should also be in the appropriate primary language.

Time Constraints on Communication

In today's busy practice environment, there is simply less time for each patient than there used to be. With less time for each patient, there is less time for real communication. It seems that, in most patient examinations, there is just enough time for information gathering, and barely enough for that. Given this time constraint, it becomes all the more imperative that you gather as much information as possible from the patient before you meet with him/her.

As your time is the most precious resource in your practice, you want to use it at maximal efficiency. As in any integrated process, the goal is to use the most precious resource most efficiently. In your office, this means doing as many jobs as possible before the key resource is used, so that resource can concentrate and deliver only the service that it is designed to provide. The most valuable resource in a doctor's office is the physician's time. As such, the challenge is to do as much of the generic information gathering from the patient as possible before you are called in, so that your time is spent asking the key medical questions and performing a physical examination.

By doing so, you will be able to review the answers to these more generic questions before meeting with the patient. You can then get a good idea of what the key issues are before even stepping in the room with the patient. This will allow you maximal "real communication" time in your consult. Ideally, you will take better histories and understand your patient's health much more thoroughly this way, without using any more of your time.

How do you achieve this efficiency? Answer the questions in the self-assessment checklist at the end of this chapter, and consider using our mock-up patient questionnaire that follows. These will give you the tools you will need to make your communications system more efficient.

Informed Consent

The second major challenge in managing communication risks continues to be securing adequate informed consent in surgical or diagnostic procedures. Despite the extensive risk management efforts over the past 15 years, this area still represents a significant portion of communication-related claims.

We suspect the fault in this area lies with individual physicians, not with the consent forms themselves. Not only should patients have witnesses to sign forms, the physician should make a separate chart note about explaining the procedure to the patient. Further, the physician should be absolutely certain that the patient understands what the physician is saying.

Physician liability in the area of informed consent often arises because the doctor fails to tell patients about treatment options other than the option for which he or she wants the patient's consent. In other cases, physicians are found liable when a spouse or other family member with a vested interest in the treatment of the patient is not made aware of the risks of a procedure or is not given other options of treatment. The following case study demonstrates both of these failures.

Case Study

Surgeon Jack Confidant saw Mary, a 28-year-old woman with a history of excessive vaginal bleeding. He believed that she required a hysterectomy, and he clearly explained the procedure to her. He did not, however, involve her husband Mark in the conversations, and he never discussed other treatment options (such as medications).

The operation proceeded smoothly and there were no postoperative complications. Months later, Mary sued successfully for defectively authorized surgery even though there were no complications. The courts upheld the claim of damages on the basis of lack of total information in the informed consent.

The surgeon made two mistakes in obtaining informed consent. First, he failed to ask the patient if he could involve the her husband in the discussions. This was a mistake not only in terms of informed consent but because of her husband's interest in the reproductive ability of his spouse. More generally, this was an error because, by leaving her husband out of the loop, the surgeon only increased the chances that the couple would be dissatisfied with her care. The surgeon also failed to provide the patient or her spouse with an explanation of other treatment options. As most states' informed consent laws require the physician to tell the patient about the benefits and risks of alternative treatments, this a common and potentially liability-creating mistake.

A new and potentially disturbing area of informed consent risk involves genetic testing. There are now a number of conditions, including colon cancer for example, that may have some identifiable genetic basis. It is extremely important that, if you are going to screen the patient for genetic disease, you obtain informed consent regarding these tests. This may become even more important under new healthcare reform rules. Another vial of blood to the laboratory does not seem like much at the time. When the patient, however, finds out that he has been screened for genetic disease, and that those results are not only available to him but also to his employers or insurers at some point, he is bound to be angry. Anger, in many cases, leads to lawsuits.

There already have been a number of cases in which physicians have been sued for ordering unwanted tests, when the test results have influenced the socioeconomic status of the patient. This area will continue to grow over the next decade. Although physicians may believe that they are providing the best medicine for their patients, they must protect themselves by carefully explaining these procedures in advance (including the possible misuse of the information) and obtaining patients' prior written consent.

Recommendations

When obtaining patients' informed consent, make sure to do the following:

1. Have the consent form signed and witnessed.

2. Make sure that patients understand what they are signing.

3. Involve close family members/spouses, and make sure they understand the process as well.

4. Explain the benefits and risks of alternative treatments and diagnostic tests in addition to the one(s) you are recommending.

5. In deciding which risks to include in your discussion, explain all risks considered possible by your specialty. Read the literature, and be aware of what colleagues are explaining.

6. In deciding which alternatives to include in your discussion, explain those considered reasonable by your specialty. Again, read the literature, and be aware of what colleagues are including in their discussions.

7. Avoid the tendency to leave out explanatory discussion because you think that patients will not understand it. It is better to assume that they will comprehend; you will be providing better care and have less risk of liability.

8. Be aware that informed consent laws apply not only to procedures, but also to prescription drugs. There is no need to get written consent for every prescription, but it is essential to explain drug risks, side effects, and contraindications. And make sure to note the discussion in the chart.

Physician-To-Physician Communication

A third area of communication risk relates to correspondence between physicians or other healthcare professionals including NPs or PAs. The most common scenario resulting in mistakes in patient care (and often in liability) is where one clinician fails to transmit information to a covering clinician. This may be a risk for you. Ask yourself the following:

- Do you have a well-defined mechanism of transferring patient information to the other clinicians in your office and in the hospital?

- When you receive information from another healthcare professional, do you read it, or do you rely on a verbal summary from your colleague?

- If you do not get along with a referring clinician, do you tend to not listen to him/her? If so, it is that much more important that you read his/her notes carefully.

- Are the reports of referring clinicians legible and understandable to you? Sometimes or always?

- Are your reports likely to be understood by other clinicians? Sometimes or always?

- Do you get the information you need from other clinicians promptly, or is there a delay because their reports are dictated? Do you think you are holding up other doctors this way?

The following case study demonstrates the risks of physician-physician communication.

Case Study

Dr. Sheila Goldstone was leaving for her vacation Saturday afternoon as soon as she completed her hospital rounds. Harry, a 60-year-old man with a history of cardiac failure, complained of mild nausea and increasing abdominal pain. Leaving a note in the chart concerning his new symptoms, Dr. Goldstone paged her colleague Dr. Bob Roberts, who was covering for the group on the weekend. Bob was swamped with two new admissions, but promised to check on Harry later that day. Bob was not as concerned with Harry's condition at 4 PM as Sheila had been, but he put in a request for a surgical consult.

Unfortunately, no one on call for surgery followed up on the request. The floor coordinator was out sick, and the head nurse had two floors to cover. At 9 AM, a general surgeon did see Harry and diagnosed small bowel obstruction with perforation. His condition continued to deteriorate, and he died after surgery.

Lawyers for Harry's estate successfully argued that both internists were responsible for the delay in diagnosis and treatment leading to his death.

Dr. Goldstone's failure to impress upon her colleague the potential seriousness of the situation resulted in Dr. Roberts not following up with the surgeon. Dr. Goldstone's particular high level of concern here should have been more clearly communicated to Dr. Roberts. A routine note or mention to your colleague may not be a strong enough communication when you are concerned about preventing a potential emergency.

Recommendation
Consider a "Level of Concern" grading system for communications to other clinicians who are covering your patients: "A" for highest priority (high risk patients), "B" for average priority, and "C" for lower priority.

Chapter 5:
Self-Assessment Checklist

How does your communication appear to your patients? To answer this question, you might consider hiring actors or interns to "act" as patients and then videotape your interactions.

If you are a golfer, swimmer, or tennis player, you must be aware of the techniques of videotaping your physical motions to improve your skills. It is hard to know what your golf stroke looks like and correct your problems without seeing yourself on tape. Think about applying the same approach to your patient communication skills. With video camera costs so low, you might easily install one in your consultation room and use actors or real patients (if their informed consent is given). Then at your leisure, view the recordings with either a close friend or spouse, preferably someone not in the medical field.

When analyzing the recording, ask yourself: How do you present yourself? Can you be understood? What about your choice of words, tone of voice? Do you appear rushed or disinterested? Do you appear sympathetic or insensitive? How is your body language? Do you make eye contact with your patient? Do you smile and nod appropriately?

To improve efficiency in information gathering, free your time and improve doctor-patient communication, consider the following questions:

- Do your new patients fill out questionnaires in advance before you see them?

- Does your office staff help?

- Could you automate the information-gathering process? Many adults today are used to computer questions on a tablet which interacts with your EMR.

- Could you save five minutes of each patient visit by collecting information in your waiting room and have it printed or on a tablet before you see each patient? Or perhaps even have patients print out and complete forms before they arrive at your office?

- Could insurance questions be incorporated into each visit questionnaire? In this era of managed care, patients have more of these questions for doctors than ever.

- Do you offer pamphlets on common ailments for patients to read in the waiting room before your examination? Many of these are available from national specialty societies.

- Do you have a separate viewing room where patients could watch videos explaining procedures or treatments, so they become educated before meeting with you?

Chapter 5- References

1. Levinson W, Roter DL, et al. Physician—patient communication: the relationship with malpractice claims among primary care physicians and surgeons. *JAMA*. 1997; 277(7):553-559.

2. Levinson W, Roter DL, et al. Physician—patient communication: the relationship with malpractice claims among primary care physicians and surgeons. *JAMA*. 1997; 277(7):553-559.

3. Levinson W, Roter DL, et al. Physician—patient communication: the relationship with malpractice claims among primary care physicians and surgeons. *JAMA*. 1997; 277(7):553-559.

Managing High-Risk Communication Areas

In a clinician's practice, there are a number of areas in which strong communication skills are especially important. Communication failures in these circumstances are either particularly common or extraordinarily dangerous in terms of patient care and/or malpractice. In this chapter, we will address a number of common high-risk communication areas including how to handle troublesome patients, how to discuss bad outcomes, and how to communicate effectively in the single patient encounter.

Communicating With Difficult Patients

One of the greatest challenges facing the clinician is to communicate with difficult patients in a way that fosters accurate diagnosis and facilitates quality treatment. Unfortunately, there is no one way to deal with difficult patients, probably because there are so many types of difficult patients. In this section, we will address four common types of difficult patients and how to communicate with them to improve their care and limit liability.

• The Disruptive Patient
Disruptive patients are always a risk-management problem. Particularly with violent patients or patients under the influence of alcohol or drugs, it is essential that you and your staff have a protocol for dealing with the situation. Although violence may only be a real concern in emergency departments, a disruptive patient can present anywhere, as the following case study demonstrates.

Case Study

Martha was in treatment for renal failure for several years in New York. When her son-in-law and daughter were transferred to Los Angeles, she moved to California to be near them. She was referred to a dialysis center in Los Angeles near her new home. A difficult and demanding patient who was ill at ease in her new surroundings, Martha disrupted the entire facility upon each visit. The staff tried to calm her each time, as did the physician who spoke to her sympathetically.

After a few months, there was little change in her behavior. The physician again warned Martha that her behavior may result in her no longer being welcome at his office. He noted all discussions with her in the chart. She acted out again at her next visit. The other patients and staff were so upset that the supervising nephrologist refused to treat her further. Martha then sued for abandonment, although he had referred her to another center.

The court found for the physician, saying Martha's own actions caused the breakdown of the physician-patient relationship. Therefore, there was no abandonment. The court noted that not only had the physician repeatedly warned her and given her six weeks' notice of discharge, but had referred her to another center.

This case illustrates a number of tactics for dealing with a disruptive patient. One should communicate sympathetically with the patient, to try to curb the behavior at the outset, as the physician did in this case. Often, these patients are seeking attention. A positive talk by staff, or better yet, the physician, can prevent problems. Sterner warnings are appropriate when the patient continues with disruptive behavior. The patient's disruptive behavior and concomitant discussions should be noted in the patient's chart. This is an invaluable tool in a defense against any claim the patient may later bring forth.

Also, it should be noted that in a critical situation (as in the case of a dialysis patient above, where discontinuation of care is life-threatening), when referring a patient to another center, the other center needs to acknowledge acceptance of the patient. Otherwise, patient abandonment could still be alleged.

- ### The Patient Who Refuses Treatment
The best strategy for dealing with these patients is to clearly communicate to them the risks and benefits of refusing the treatment at hand; then note the discussion in the chart. Better yet, follow our recommendations in the last chapter on informed consent, and get the patient to sign a form indicating his/her refusal. (See a sample form in the self-assessment checklist.) Also, with the patient's consent, involve spouse or family members, if possible.

The same principles and recommendations apply for dealing with the patient who insists on leaving the hospital against your advice. Disclose all risks, document the discussion in the chart, and have the patient sign the hospital's "signed out against medical advice" form.

- ### The Doubting Patient
Often, the patients who become most combative in the final analysis are not so difficult at the outset. Rather than the patient who refuses treatment or testing, it may be the patient who subtly doubts or questions your choices who is more likely to end up suing you for malpractice. How do you recognize these "doubting patients?"

The patients who overtly ask for a second opinion are the least difficult. Simply send that patient to another physician, preferably a specialist, for a second opinion. If you do not, and there is anything less than a perfect outcome, you will be a ripe target for malpractice action.

Other doubting patients will not be so obvious in their suspicions. You may have to read between the lines of their conversation and interpret their body language as well. For example, a patient or her family member may ask you if she should see a specialist (or another type of specialist). Your first response may be to calm the patient and family and reassure them that you see and treat this type of condition all the time. Even though this response may be justifiable (you may well see and treat this condition routinely), your competence is not the issue here.

What this patient/family member may be trying to tell you is that they prefer to see a specialist (or another type of specialist). Whether or not you believe the patient really needs the referral, try to make it happen. Although this may be more difficult in managed care settings, a referral is good patient care and smart risk management.

• The Patient with Last-Second Recollection

Those physicians who deal with elderly people will recognize the phenomena of the last-minute patient recollection of a major problem after you have almost completed the visit. When Columbo, the TV detective, asked questions as he was apparently leaving, the person to whom the question was addressed was caught off guard. In your office, when the patient asks questions as they walk out the door, it is you who are caught off guard.

Faced with this situation, you have two alternatives: either you delay their exit and further stretch your schedule, or you brush off the question with a quick answer. The delay costs you time, aggravation, and staff salaries. The quick answer may cost you patient confidence and a lawsuit, as demonstrated by the following case study.

Case Study

Nellie, a 75-year-old widow, became so nervous about her visits to each of her many doctors, that she frequently forgot why she went in the first place. Rather than writing down her chief complaints in advance, she tried to remember everything during her appointment with Dr. Caswell, her internist. On her last visit, Nellie remembered a low-grade pain between her shoulder blades, just as she was leaving. Dr. Caswell received a phone call as Nellie is describing the pain. Not entirely focused on her description, he reassured her it was probably just a pulled muscle and that she shouldn't worry about it.

As the pain increased over the next few days, Nellie was concerned but remembered that Dr. Caswell had reassured her not to worry. After three days, the pain grew much worse, and she called the rescue squad who took her to a local emergency room. She was admitted after a CT scan showed a dissecting aortic aneurysm, and she died two days later.

This case demonstrates the difficulty of dealing with the last-second recollection. Dr. Caswell did not take the time to consider Nellie's final complaints about the pain in her back. He was too rushed and distracted to take these last-second statements seriously. Unfortunately, this turned out to be a tragic mistake.

Recommendation

One technique that may alleviate this problem is to ask patients as they enter your examination room, "How can I help you?" This is a nonthreatening approach that usually elicits the patient's real chief complaint. Once the patient is finished talking, you can guide the remainder of the allotted time for history and physical examination.

Communicating Bad Outcomes

Communicating bad outcomes to patients is one of the most difficult tasks a physician must perform. Perhaps because it is so difficult, many clinicians communicate poorly with patients and their families after a bad outcome. Another contributing factor to the miscommunication after bad outcomes has been the advice of risk managers of a previous era.

Classical risk-management teaching previously advocated that the less said about a bad outcome to anyone, the better. Insurance companies, lawyers, and hospital risk managers had all been trained to keep any problems very quiet. Only behind closed doors, with certain qualified individuals, were you allowed to discuss the case. "Not even with your partners or colleagues," you were warned. Did all of this secrecy really make sense? Did it improve patient relations or prevent litigation? No.

Today's risk management approach to dealing with poor outcomes is to communicate with the patient and family directly and sympathetically, as soon after the outcome as possible. Although many risk managers still insist on avoiding an apology in all situations, there may be instances when you believe that one is appropriate. If so, use language that shows an acknowledgment of the reality of regret and tragedy ("I am sorry that this happened" or "I am sorry that you are in such pain") rather than language that shows an acknowledgment of malfeasance or wrongdoing. Beyond this, consider the following recommendations when communicating bad outcomes to patients and their families.

Recommendations

- When things go wrong, or you suspect a patient is unhappy, do not give in to the natural inclination to avoid him/her or his/her family. Rather, give the patient as much time as he/she wants. A genuine interest in trying to resolve problems and create the best treatment plan going forward should be your attitude. Patients will forgive honest mistakes, and your extra time and concern can turn any situation in your favor.

- In communicating with patients and family, direct sympathetic phrasing is best. Consider something like this: "I am sorry that you have suffered complications. These are the problems we are facing, and here is our plan." Of course, proper eye contact and other body language is essential in communicating a sympathetic yet strong image.

- In meeting with patients and family after a bad outcome, do not bring attorneys or other risk management officials. The meeting should be about building bridges and healing pain. However, if potential claimants request to bring an attorney, you should also have legal representation.

Communicating in the Single Encounter

The single encounter with a patient provides an atmosphere in which the clinician may get only one chance to be "right" or to make an appropriate diagnosis. In this situation, the stakes are much higher, as is the risk of miscommunication. Although the single encounter is common emergency department practice, the scenario also occurs in other types of practices. Does it occur in your practice? Does it occur during a new patient visit? During a phone consultation? During an outpatient clinic or emergency room visit?

Recommendation

To maximize patient care and for liability protection in one-time encounters, documentation is critical. You must document not only what you observed in the patient, but also what you did not observe. Further, make sure to note what you told the patient or family about follow-up and what you found or did not find on physical examination, x-ray examination, or laboratory tests. Also document the existence of a referral, if applicable. Although documentation is always critical to proper risk management, it is especially so in the high-risk single-encounter situation.

Chapter 6:
Self-Assessment Checklist

- **Disruptive Patients**

Consider making a thorough analysis of your interactions with disruptive patients. After any confrontational interaction, write down your notes immediately. Ask yourself the following:

1. Is your behavior with disruptive patients appropriate?

2. Do you become angry or noncommunicative?

3. We all know how we act in conflict with spouses and children. Do you behave differently in your patient-centered conflicts?

4. Is anything you are saying or doing making your patients into difficult patients?

5. Is your office user-friendly? Are there enough seats and reading material for patients kept waiting? Do you have a television set or a coffee pot? Would a personalized computer interview screen not only give you needed information, but keep your patients occupied and happy? Are your gowns large enough? Does your receptionist smile or frown? Do you stick to your schedule?

6. If your patients know they are on a prepaid plan, do they see you as just wanting to get them out the door? There is more and more being written in the lay press about capitation. How would you feel about being a capitated patient in your practice? Recent popular magazine articles are giving instructions to patients about how to trap physicians in managed care guidelines. Could this be a problem for you? "The satisfied patient rarely sues, but a dissatisfied one will find a reason to."

7. When you and your patients have conflicting values, how do you handle this? Are you psychologically and professionally prepared to discharge a patient? Do you have a written plan? If not, even verbal conflicts can escalate into lawsuits. If you are going to discharge a patient, make sure that you are giving him or her enough time and notice to find another physician, and consider abandonment issues, especially if a critical illness is involved. Have a policy for forwarding charts.

• The Patient Who Refuses Treatment

Use the form on the following page for a patient who refuses treatment. It could save you a malpractice lawsuit down the road.

REFUSAL TO UNDERGO TREATMENT

Name _____

Age _____

Date _____

Location _____

Dr. _____ has explained to me in detail the
foreseeable risks associated with a _____, and
I have elected not to undergo a _____.

Dr. _____ has explained to me in detail that the
foreseeable risks associated with my electing not to undergo a
_____ are _____.

_____
Patient   Date

_____
Legal Representative (if patient cannot understand)

_____
Witness   Date

Method of Participation for Obtaining CME Credit for Chapters 5 and 6

There are no fees to receive CME credit for participating in this activity. If you wish to receive continuing education credit, please do the following:

1. Review the objectives, statement of need, and disclosure information.

2. Read the indicated chapters.

3. To obtain the maximum benefit from this activity, you are encouraged to complete the self-assessment checklist at the end of each chapter, as applicable, and formulate an action plan based on each self-assessment exercise.

4. Go online using the URL below and complete the self-assessment (achieving a passing score of 70 percent) and the activity evaluation. If you do not achieve a passing score in three attempts, please contact CEServices@cme.com to have your account reset. Upon passing the assessment and completing the evaluation, you will be able to print or save your certificate of credit.

www.academycme.org/actID=19GU163
activity code: 19GU163

Managing Privacy Risks: HIPAA and Beyond

Some of the most important legislation affecting how physicians practice are the privacy protections passed by Federal and State governments, beginning with the Health Insurance Portability and Accountability Act, commonly known as "HIPAA" in 1996 and its Privacy Rule, which went into effect in 2003.

According to Congress, HIPAA's purpose is "to improve portability and continuity of health insurance coverage in the group and individual markets, to combat waste, fraud, and abuse in health insurance and healthcare delivery, to promote the use of medical savings accounts, to improve access to long-term care services and coverage, to simplify the administration of health insurance, and for other purposes." One of these "other purposes" is certainly to protect the individual's privacy right in their confidential medical information.

Once this statute became law and parallel state legislation was enacted, a new and important risk faced practicing physicians: the risk of violating the privacy protections now imposed on physicians and their offices.

As our goal is to give you practical knowledge and advice on how to reduce this risk in your practice, we think it is imperative that we first familiarize you with basic concepts surrounding privacy protection including the impact that the Health Information Technology for Economic and Clinical Health Act ("HITECH Act"), passed in 2009,has had on HIPAA rules.

1. What "privacy" means
There are many ways to define "privacy" – it is a broad concept

that includes many meanings. Here, we are really focusing on "information privacy": the ability to control how data about the patient is collected, used and disclosed.

Even within this definition, there are various challenges. Specifically, you will need to address both information privacy policies and practices (like the kind your hospital, managed care organization or group practice has developed), and technical, physical and administrative information security practices that protect computerized data systems.

2. Why protect privacy?

Of course, the obvious answer to this question is "because you have to." Without the legal burden, however, you might not spend the time, inconvenience and expense associated with data protection. However, you should. The duty to protect patient confidentiality goes beyond a legal duty to a professional responsibility. Consider these points:

- As we noted in the introduction, protecting patients' privacy is inherently "the right thing to do." Respect for patients means respecting their wishes about uses and disclosures of their health information.

- Privacy protection is necessary for good outcomes. Patients will not receive good care if concerns about privacy make them afraid to reveal information to health providers.

- Privacy protection is necessary for the overall public health system, too. Public health surveillance, health outcomes (cost effectiveness) studies, and healthcare research all depend on accurate data.

Privacy is not just a nicety; it is essential for the health system to function at all.

3. What federal law (HIPAA) requires – overview

As we explained above, HIPAA is an abbreviation for Health Insurance Portability and Accountability Act. As it applies here, HIPAA aims to improve accountability in part through what it calls administrative simplification – a term that roughly translates as "promoting efficiency."

The principal means of promoting efficiency is increased use of information technology. Compared to other parts of the economy, health care is relatively "uncomputerized" – particularly in its use of paper for health records. As HIPAA requires more use of computer systems, it also addresses worries about compromises of patient information.

- *Three standards, three parts*
  HIPAA has three health information standards and three associated regulations or "rules". These rules are as follows:

  A. standardize formats for all computer-to-computer information exchanges (the "transactions standard");

  B. standardize "identifiers" for health providers, health plans and patients;

  C. implement information system security standards and privacy standards.

- *Who is covered?*
  Almost every organization that provides or pays for health services, or exchanges health data of any kind, is within the reach of HIPAA. All healthcare providers (physicians, nurses, etc.), all healthcare facilities, all health plans (HMOs, insurers), and all health information clearinghouses are covered entities.

  The law extends protections, or "rights", to every patient whose information is collected, used or disclosed by such covered entities. It imposes responsibilities on the workforce of a covered entity in order to secure those rights (including all employees and volunteers). The law reaches even to the business associates of healthcare institutions – that is, to any companies that handle healthcare information on a covered entity's behalf.

- *What is covered?*
  Under HIPAA, protected health information (PHI), and ePHI (electronically stored PHI) is very broadly defined. Anything related to the "past, present or future physical or mental health condition" of a person is covered by the law's standards. Only adequately de-identified information – where it would be virtually impossible to identify the person to whom the data refers – is unprotected. While HIPAA transaction, identifier and security rules cover only electronic information, its privacy provisions apply to all paper, electronic or oral communications of PHI.

4. HIPAA Requirements in Practice

Obviously, this short chapter is not designed to replace a full-scale HIPAA compliance manual for your practice. It is designed to provide a basic outline of rules and responsibilities. Your practice should be guided by an appropriate HIPAA practice consultant.

- *Notification of rights*
  HIPAA requires covered entities, including the physician practices, to provide patients with a notice of privacy practices. The Notice must describe, in general terms, how organizations will protect health information, and specify the patient's right to:

  1. gain access to and, if desired, obtain a copy of his/her own health records;

  2. request corrections of errors that the patient finds (or to include a statement of disagreement about errors the institution refuses to change);

  3. receive an accounting of how their information has been used (including a list of the persons and institutions to whom/which it has been disclosed);

  4. request limits on access to, and additional protections for, particularly sensitive information;

5. request confidential communications (by alternative means or at alternative locations) of particularly sensitive information;

6. complain to the facility's privacy officer if there are problems; and

7. pursue the complaint with the US Department of Health and Human Services' Office of Civil Rights if the problems are not satisfactorily resolved.

A copy of the Notice must be provided the first time a patient sees a direct treatment provider, and any time thereafter when requested. Health plans and insurers must also provide periodic Notices.

- *Acknowledgements and Authorizations*
  On that first visit, treatment providers must also make a "good faith effort" to obtain a written acknowledgement, confirming that a copy of the Notice was obtained. This is the moment when providers should discuss patients' particular privacy questions and concerns.

  In emergency situations, the acknowledgement process can be deferred. (Note that the acknowledgement does not affirm that the patient understands what is in the Notice, just receipt of it.) The requirement for a signed acknowledgement replaces the consent requirement in an earlier version of the Privacy Rule. Covered entities may still ask the patient to sign a consent form, but the practice is not entirely optional under HIPAA.

  No additional documentation is required from the patient to use or disclose information for basic functions, like treatment and payment, or for a broad range of other core healthcare operations. However, patients must sign a supplemental authorization before information can be used for "extra" purposes like research, or certain kinds of marketing and fundraising.

Healthcare institutions cannot condition treatment or payment for healthcare services on receiving a patient's authorization for such supplemental uses.

- *Four information categories covered*
  The general rule under HIPAA is a simple one: if a person has a right to make a healthcare decision, then he/she has the right to control information associated with that decision.

  Children and those who are incompetent may have decisions about both health care and health information made by a personal representative. (Typically, the personal representative is the parent in the case of a child.).

  One way to think about use and disclosure of protected health information under HIPAA is by putting it into four categories:

  1. covered by an acknowledgement of Notice (and perhaps an optional consent), which includes routine treatment, payment and other healthcare operations;

  2. requiring a supplemental authorization, such as research, marketing or fundraising;

  3. requiring an opportunity to agree or object to a practice, but no consent or authorization; and

  4. not requiring even an opportunity to agree or object.

  We have already discussed the first two. The third of these categories includes uses for facility directories, and disclosures to those involved in a person's care.

  The fourth category includes PHI uses where there is no opportunity for the patient to agree or object to the use of the information. This occurs in certain circumstances, such as:

1. for public health activities;

2. for victims of abuse, neglect or domestic violence;

3. for health oversight activities;

4. for judicial or administrative proceedings;

5. for law enforcement;

6. about deceased persons (including organ and tissue donations);

7. where permitted by an IRB or Privacy Board waiver, for research;

8. to avert a serious, imminent threat to public safety;

9. certain specialized government functions (e.g., national security, military, corrections); or

10. anything else required by law.

Individuals would be entitled to an accounting of such disclosures, though that accounting might be temporarily suspended in certain circumstances.

- *Minimum necessary standard*
  Beyond all the above categories, HIPAA imposes a "minimum necessary standard" on persons who deal with health information: collection, use and disclosure should be no greater than necessary to complete a work-related task.

  The minimum necessary standard does not apply to health practitioners engaged in treatment. The regulations try to avoid interfering in the daily practice of delivering health care. (That said, you, as a physician, are under a moral and professional requirement to limit information exchange to what is needed for good treatment.)

  Healthcare facilities are under an obligation to integrate a minimum necessary standard into their policies and procedures for everyone other than treatment providers. That includes administrative rules as well as, where available, computer-enforced access controls. HIPAA extends extra protections for especially sensitive information, notably psychotherapy notes, which require a supplemental authorization for release.

- *Institutional policies and procedures*
  To be sure, it is a long list of standards and categories, and not one you should attempt to memorize. It is sufficient to have a sense of the overall structure. (For a more intensive exposure to the requirements, consult with an experienced HIPAA advisor).

  You do need to know that every healthcare facility must put in place privacy policies that reflect HIPAA's requirements, and, if they are stricter, the requirements of state law. Those policies must include sanctions for employees that violate them, including termination for serious or repeated violations.

  Institutions must designate a privacy officer, who will have the responsibility for enforcing the rules, as well as supervising (or handling directly) the procedures to handle requests for information access, corrections to records, accountings of disclosures, processing complaints and so forth.

  Institutions must also include privacy requirements in their contracts with business associates.

  Finally, all employees (and volunteers) must be educated about privacy practices in a manner "appropriate" to their job responsibilities.

  Many of HIPAA's "new" protections are actually "old" ones that already are a part of your state's laws or required by norms of professional practice. Unfortunately, those rules and norms often were ignored and HIPAA was enacted on the Federal level to fill the void.

- *Sanctions for violations*
  The most important sanction for a physician is not written in any law book -- it is the loss of business

if patients lose confidence in its information practices. In the competitive market that has come with managed care, few healthcare practices can afford to lose patients for any reason. Further, no practice can afford to keep a worker who fails to observe the privacy rules, given the substantial consequences for violations.

Beyond this business reason, HIPAA includes substantial civil and criminal penalties to encourage compliance. These penalties range from $100 per violation up to $250,000 and 10 years in prison. The harshest penalties attend deliberate misuse, particularly for sale or use of information for personal gain, commercial advantage or malicious harm. Persons convicted for such activities can expect to visit a federal prison. State penalties may also apply, along with possible disciplinary actions by certification bodies (e.g., loss of license to practice).

Failures that result from accidental disclosures are unlikely to be fined, much less result in jail time, provided reasonable steps are taken to fix the violation as soon as possible.

5. HIPAA and state law

As noted above, states have laws that also address information protection. Some have broad privacy laws, including privacy provisions in the state constitution. Almost all have laws that cover health information specifically.

In many cases, the requirements of state law are even stricter than the federal requirements. While HIPAA adds its protections to state law, any state laws that are more protective of health privacy remain in force.

Be sure to meet with a HIPAA consultant or healthcare attorney in your state to see what your state requires in this area.

6. Civil liability

The HIPAA regulations themselves do not grant a private right of enforcement to patients who believe themselves injured by a presumed violation of HIPAA. This means that an attorney representing a patient cannot merely file suit, alleging a violation of HIPAA. But this also does not mean there will not be an increase in privacy and confidentiality violation lawsuits. In fact, many prominent personal injury attorneys have already announced they expect this will become a large part of their practice. They will attempt to use the HIPAA regulations as standard of care when they file state approved lawsuits under privacy laws. A recent Wisconsin case illustrates this possibility.

Case Study: "Helpful Disclosure Still Liable"

The defendant EMT and three other members of the volunteer fire department responded to an emergency 911 call at the plaintiff's residence regarding an overdose or possible overdose. After treating the patient and transporting her to the hospital, the EMT went home and later spoke to a friend about the incident. The EMT did not know the patient personally, but knew a friend of hers and, in hoping the friend could help the patient, relayed the story. The friend then visited the plaintiff's home where she revealed some of the new information to the plaintiff's family and then to hospital personnel.

The plaintiff successfully sued the EMT, and volunteer fire department, for violation of privacy – a suit that was upheld on appeal.

This case illustrates how even in very small cases, state law can be a powerful weapon when it comes to invasion of privacy and possible defamation (see below for more on state law). "Good intentions" were not a successful defense, and not having a written policy in this area could also subject you to HIPAA violations, even if the lawsuit was brought under state law. HIPAA is the first law to bring a standard of patient privacy protection to all 50 states. The publicity surrounding HIPAA, and the need to inform all patients, means that public expectations and awareness are now raised among patients and attorneys.

7. What your institution requires

Beyond HIPAA and even state law, the healthcare institutions with which you are affiliated may have even more onerous requirements. Be sure to work with these institutions' privacy officers to ensure that your office is complying with their procedures as well.

8. You are also a patient

Physicians have healthcare needs too, of course – we see our own healthcare providers from time to time. Another important reason to be more familiar with HIPAA is to understand the privacy protections for our own health information. Your day-to-day behavior determines the privacy of others' health information. And, somewhere out there, the actions of other healthcare workers will determine how much privacy you have.

Recommendations

1. Generate an appropriate Privacy Notice and, on a patient's first visit, obtain a written acknowledgement, confirming that a copy of the Notice was obtained. This is the moment when providers should discuss patients' particular privacy questions and concerns.

2. Consult with a medical practice consultant and/or healthcare attorney to implement procedures and policies for your office to comply with HIPAA and state law requirements.

3. Speak with the privacy officers of each healthcare institution with which you are affiliated. Make the appropriate changes to your office to be in compliance with their privacy procedures.

The HITECH Act's Impact on HIPAA Rules

The passage of the HITECH Act, part of the American Recovery and Reinvestment Act of 2009, marked a new phase of HIPAA regulation. The sweeping changes under the HITECH Act closed many of the gaps that complicated enforcement and added regulations that increased accountability and penalties for violations. These were changes that many in the healthcare industry applauded for giving regulations the clarity and teeth necessary to enable progress in the push for better privacy and security.

Here, we will address very briefly Subtitle D of HITECH amending the privacy and security rules under HIPAA. HIPAA's privacy and security rules established floors of confidentiality and security protections for patients' demographic and health information in all forms—paper, oral, and electronic. The development of health information technology (for example, electronic health records, personal health records, health information exchanges) up until 2009 had resulted in additional risks; HITECH was intended to build on the privacy and security rules to address these new risks.

Specifically, the HITECH Act impacted HIPAA in a number of significant ways. The two most important, in the authors' views are the following:

1. *Expanded HIPAA's reach to "business associates."*
   Under the privacy rule, a business associate is a person who provides a function on behalf of a covered entity (other than as part of the covered entity's workforce) that involves the use of protected health information (PHI). Examples of this type of business associate include billing services, transcription services, and answering services. A business associate is also a person who provides specified services involving the use of PHI to a covered entity. The specified services are legal, actuarial, accounting, consulting, data aggregation, management, administrative, accreditation, and financial services.

   Business associates may use and disclose PHI, but only in compliance with the business associate agreement evidencing the business associate's promise to maintain the confidentiality and security of PHI. Under existing law, business associates only have contractual liability with the covered entity via the business associate agreement. As of February 2010, business associates must comply with the security rule and will be subject to government enforcement.[1]

This is obviously a massive expansion of the reach of HIPAA to nearly any type of related service to a health provider in the normal course of business.

2. *Increased HIPAA enforcement*

The HITECH Act also increased enforcement of HIPAA by the federal and state government. These changes include the following:

State attorneys general can bring enforcement action for violations of federal HIPAA regulations.

- Employees and individuals are subject to HIPAA's criminal penalties.

- The Department of Health and Human Services (HHS) must conduct audits of covered entities and business associates.

- HHS must investigate complaints of willful neglect, and if substantiated, HHS must impose a statutory penalty of at least $10,000 to $50,000 per violation.

- HHS and state attorneys general can pursue civil HIPAA violations in cases where criminal penalty could attach, but the Department of Justice declines to pursue.

- Individuals can recover a percentage of penalties imposed or settlement proceeds from HIPAA investigations based on their complaints.[2]

As you will see in the next chapter, the HITECH changes above, along with a more aggressive Department of Justice, have resulted in a new wave of criminal actions against violators of HIPAA.

HIPPAA since our 2016 Edition

There have been a number of significant developments in the HIPAA world since our last publication of this monograph in 2016 and there certainly will be more after this edition goes to print. For continuing education on the area, we highly recommend the website www.hipaajournal.com. We used it as reference for much of the discussion below. Also, as we recommend repeatedly in this and the next chapter on HIPPAA compliance, if you are tasked to make sure your medical practice is compliant under federal, state and local law, working with a knowledgeable healthcare attorney is paramount.

In the 2013 Final Omnibus Rule, new HIPPAA regulations were enacted, including guidelines on how ePHI must be accessed and communicated in a medically related environment. This legislation gave patients further rights to know how their medical information is used, as well as more control of that information.

A few changes to the environment included:[3]

- HIPPAA-covered entities must now restrict the information flow to a private network, monitor information on the network and take measures to prevent employees from communicating or transferring such ePHI beyond the network.

- Reporting procedures covering data breaches were established.

- The Office for Civil Rights (OCR) can conduct audits on HIPAA-covered entities to ensure they comply with the regulations. When avoidable breaches of ePHI are discovered, the OCR has the authority to impose financial penalties and bring criminal charges against the negligent entity.

"Bring Your Own Devices"

One of the most important issues that has developed since the 2013 Omnibus Rule has been regarding "BYODs" – i.e., physicians' and other healthcare personnel's smartphones, tablets, PCs, etc. Numerous players in the technology fields have jumped into this niche – for example, secure text messaging systems so ePHI can be texted.

The encryption area is another burgeoning area of technology that has a direct impact on how ePHI can be handled. With proper encryption, even if mobile devices are lost or stolen, no health information or personal identifiers will be disclosed. Proper encryption renders all encrypted data protected from unauthorized access, thereby ensuring that even a cyber attack or loss of device will not result in a HIPAA violation.

Not only does full encryption for data storage and communication prevent HIPAA breaches, it shows patients that an organization is fully committed to protecting their privacy.

Recommendations Regarding BYODs

An excellent primer for BYODs is found in the article "3 Do's and Don'ts of Effective HIPAA Compliance for BYOD mHealth."[4] Although the article dates from 2013, when the Omnibus Rule came out, it is still a good practical primer. The following are the quick Do's/Don'ts. For more discussion on the subject, see the endnote for the reference to this article.

DO:
1. Make sure your vendor and its sub-vendors are compliant with the HIPAA Omnibus requirements.

2. Use two levels of security upon login to enterprise apps:

- The first stage of this can be achieved by leveraging an organization's Active Directory, enabling each provider to use their same hospital system login credentials. The second stage to login security is to use a separate PIN for quick access to mobile apps while they are in active use.

3. Have the capabilities to remotely wipe a device if it is missing:

- While this is not required by HIPAA, it should be an essential administrative practice in any mobile or BYOD program.

DON'T:
1. Allow PHI or any info to be written to the mobile device:

- Though many consumer-oriented mobile messaging apps offer providers a high level of convenience in communication, they are generally not HIPAA-compliant.

2. Permit integrations with insecure file-sharing/hosting services:

- Cloud storage and file sharing services such as Dropbox, Evernote and others are not HIPAA-compliant and should not be used to transmit PHI.

3. Set it and forget it:

- Periodically audit mobile devices. All organizations should have an auditing schedule for devices that transmit work-related information to ensure they are in compliance with organization and regulatory requirements.

Conclusion

Protecting a patient's confidential information has always been a crucial part of the physician-patient relationship. Now that duty has expanded under HIPAA, state law, and healthcare institutions' policies. As a caring physician, you want your patients to have a comfort level that their personal information will be properly protected. Only then, will they feel comfortable in providing you all the information you need to give them proper patient care. Further, only then can you be sure that you will not be liable for breaches of this confidential relationship.

Chapter 7:
Self-Assessment Checklist

- On a new patient's initial visit, do you provide them with a Privacy Notice and obtain a written acknowledgement, confirming that a copy of the Notice was obtained?

- Has this Notice been reviewed by an outside consultant or attorney to be sure it complies with the latest Federal and State guidelines? Has it been approved by your affiliated healthcare institutions?

- Do you understand what HIPAA's Privacy Rule requires? There are comprehensive educational resources available on the HHS Web site, <www.hhs.gov/ocr/privacy>.

- Do you know what the Security Rule requires to protect against reasonably anticipated improper use or disclosure of electronic PHI? The Security Rule consists of 18 safeguards (administrative, physical, and technical), and for each of the three types of safeguards, there are standards (what must be done) and implementation specifications (how it must be done).

- Most importantly, have you employed a medical practice consultant and/or healthcare attorney to implement procedures and policies for your office to comply with HIPAA, state law requirements, HITECH and those of your affiliated healthcare institutions?

Chapter 7- References

1. Roop, Elizabeth S, "Pulling It Together — The HITECH Act & HIPAA" *For The Record* Vol. 21 No. 17 P. 10 (September 14, 2009). Roop, Elizabeth S. "Pulling It Together — The HITECH Act & HIPAA" For The Record Vol. 21 No. 17 P. 10 (September 14, 2009).

2. Roop, Elizabeth S, "Pulling It Together — The HITECH Act & HIPAA" *For The Record* Vol. 21 No. 17 P. 10 (September 14, 2009). Roop, Elizabeth S. "Pulling It Together — The

HITECH Act & HIPAA" For The Record Vol. 21 No. 17 P. 10 (September 14, 2009).

3. See http://www.hipaajournal.com/hipaa-explained/.

4. Pennic, Jasmine. "3 Do's and Don'ts of Effective HIPAA Compliance for BYOD & mHealth" (06/11/2013) found at http://hitconsultant.net/2013/06/11/3-dos-and-donts-of-effective-hipaa-compliance-for-byod-mhealth/.

From Congress to Court: Results and Lessons from HIPAA Litigation

In the prior chapter, we laid out the basic scope of the HIPAA rules, what the legislation and its successive regulations essentially dictate, and some high level tips on how medical professionals can best adhere to it. In this chapter, we will provide some statistics in terms of claims made under the privacy provisions. Then, we will examine some of the leading legal cases that have tried to interpret what the HIPAA rules have come to mean.

Statistics: What The Data Shows Over 16 Years

- According to the U.S. Department of Health and Human Services website www.hhs.gov, the most recent data at the time of writing this 2019 monograph showed the following: From April 14, 2003 through June 2019, 38,843 complaints had been investigated by the OCR, with no violation found in 11,828 (30 percent) and corrective action obtained (Change Achieved) in 27,015 (70 percent).[1]

- According to its enforcement highlights report, the OCR has applied corrective measures in all cases where an investigation indicates noncompliance by the covered entity or their business associate, which may include settling with the entity in lieu of imposing civil money penalties. The OCR has settled 65 such cases resulting in a total dollar amount of $102,681,582.[2]

From their report through June 30, 2019, HHS stated that the compliance issues investigated most were, in order of frequency:

1. Impermissible uses and disclosures of protected health information;

2. Lack of safeguards of protected health information;

3. Lack of patient access to their protected health information;

4. Lack of administrative safeguards of electronic protected health information.

5. Use or disclosure of more than the minimum necessary protected health information.

The most common types of covered entities that have been required to take corrective action to achieve voluntary compliance are, in order of frequency:

- General Hospitals;

- Private Practices and Physicians;

- Outpatient Facilities;

- Pharmacies; and

- Health Plans (group health plans and health insurance issuers).

Criminal Actions

OCR refers to the Department of Justice (DOJ) for criminal investigation appropriate cases involving the knowing disclosure or obtaining of protected health information in violation of the Rules. As of June 30, 2019, OCR made 750 such referrals to DOJ.[3]

Lessons to be Learned from the Data

What can the practicing physician learn from these statistics? A number of important lessons emerge:

1. The risk of having a patient complaint is a real one –

as private healthcare practices continue to be among the most frequent subjects of a complaint.

2. Meritless complaints are problematic here as they are in medical malpractice litigation in general – as evidenced here by the high number of complaints that do not warrant investigations.

3. This is an emerging area of regulation where further study and experience is needed.

Court Rulings on HIPAA

As with any new major legislation, once Congress has passed the law, the administrative agencies attempt to implement the law with various regulations and procedures. While there is typically a few year lag time, eventually the court system will become involved, as parties either sue to have elements of the law overturned or interpreted, or be compensated for some violation thereof. In this case, there is more than the federal HIPAA rules at issue, as each state has enacted privacy legislation as well. As you will see below, these rules also need state court interpretation.

Gunn v. Sound Shore Medical Center of Westchester, 772 N.Y.S.2d 714

In this New York case, the plaintiff was allegedly injured by a treadmill at a cardiac rehabilitation facility, which was owned by the defendant hospital. The plaintiff sought the names and addresses of the other patients who were at the facility at the time of the incident. The trial court agreed with the plaintiff, ordering the defendant hospital to disclose the patients' names. When the hospital appealed, the appellate court reversed the trial court's decision, stating "since disclosure of the patients' names will, in effect, reveal that they were undergoing treatment for cardiac-related conditions, such discovery is prohibited under [New York's physician-patient privilege law]."

The most interesting part of this case is that the court referred to HIPAA even though the statute was not an issue in the case. The court said, "the passage of HIPAA lends support to the conclusion that disclosure of the identity of the other patients at the center would breach the physician-patient privilege and thus should not be permitted."

This case is important as it shows how courts will use HIPAA to potentially expand the privacy protections (and liability for violations thereof) outside of HIPAA's jurisdiction. See the cases below for similar results.

Hutton v. City of Martinez, 219 F.R.D. 164 (Northern District of California, 2003)

In this personal injury case, the defendant was a police officer who shot the plaintiff in the back. The plaintiff claimed he was shot because the defendant was physically unable to pursue the plaintiff on foot. To bolster his argument, the plaintiff sought to obtain evidence of the defendant's physical condition from the defendant's workers' compensation carrier. The workers' compensation carrier, even though explicitly excluded from the definition of a "covered entity" under HIPAA, nonetheless relied on HIPAA to refuse to produce the records related to the defendant's work-related back injury. The court found the medical records to be directly relevant and held that "HIPAA does not preclude production of the medical records and workers' compensation files in response to either a discovery request, subpoena, or this court's order, under an adequate protective order."

This was interesting because of the attempted use of HIPAA by the worker's compensation carrier to shield it from having to turn over information based on privacy grounds. Although the court did not "buy" the argument in this case, it does demonstrate the potential leveraging of HIPAA rules by parties not explicitly covered by the statute.

Acara v. Banks, 470 F.3d 569, 571 (5th Cir. 2006)

This case is significant for two reasons: (1) because it is the only HIPAA case that has risen to the federal circuit court level – one level below the Supreme Court – and (2) because it clearly stated that there is no private cause of action (right to sue) under the HIPAA statute. The court said specifically: "HIPAA does not contain any express language conferring private rights upon a specific class of individuals. Instead, it focuses on regulating persons that have access to individually identifiable medical information and who conduct certain electronic health transactions. Because HIPAA specifically delegates enforcement, there is a strong indication that Congress intended to preclude private enforcement."

Based on her assumption that HIPAA allowed her a private cause of action for damages, plaintiff Margaret Acara filed a claim in Louisiana Federal Court against her physician for allegedly disclosing Acara's private medical information without her consent during a deposition. However, the trial court dismissed Acara's claims on the grounds that it did not have jurisdiction over the dispute since there was no private right of action under HIPAA. The Fifth Circuit agreed and affirmed the trial court's ruling.

Acosta v. Byrum 638 S.E.2d 246 (N.C. Ct. App. 2006)

In this case, a patient sued a psychiatrist for negligent infliction of emotional distress. The basis of the patient's claim was that the defendant psychiatrist allegedly allowed his office manager access to the plaintiff's mental health records.

At trial the court found that the plaintiff's claim did not specify what HIPAA standard the psychiatrist violated, and therefore granted summary judgment to the psychiatrist. The appeals court differed, stating that there was no need to specify what standard was violated, since the pleading need only put the psychiatrist on notice as to the basis of the claim. Thus, it found that summary judgment should not have been granted.

The appeals court also noted the plaintiff's claim here was not a HIPAA breach per se, but a common-law tort of negligent infliction of emotional distress. The plaintiff was simply using the HIPAA breach as evidence that the standard of care was not met.

Again, like the Gunn case above, the court here recognized that HIPAA may have implications beyond its specific jurisdiction. Here, the court found that a breach of HIPAA could be evidence of failure to meet the standard of care and, thus, liability to a patient in a private suit outside of HIPAA. This is an important development.

Examples of Early Criminal Indictments under HIPAA (pre-2013)

In an early action, but a sign of things to come, an indictment by a grand jury under the U.S. attorney for the Eastern District of

Arkansas signaled an aggressive change in direction regarding federal prosecution of HIPAA violators. In that case, a nurse pleaded guilty to a single count of a HIPAA violation. Andrea Smith, who was employed at the Northeast Arkansas Clinic in Jonesboro, Arkansas, accessed the private information of a clinic patient on Nov. 28, 2006, according to a news release. She gave the information to her husband who allegedly called the patient and threatened to use the information against the patient in an upcoming legal proceeding, the release said. With her guilty plea, charges against her husband and another charge against Smith were dropped, the release said.

Jane Duke, the U.S. attorney who brought the charge, said in the release that the Justice Department is serious about enforcing the criminal HIPAA statute, even when it comes to charging individuals. "What every HIPAA-covered entity needs to realize and reinforce to its employees is that the privacy provisions of HIPAA are serious and have significant consequences if they are violated," In the release, Duke noted at the time (2008) that criminal enforcement of HIPAA "is a fairly new concept."[4]

In the same time period (2009), the same U.S. attorney (Jane Duke) led an investigation where a physician and two former employees at St. Vincent Infirmary Medical Center in Little Rock, Arkansas, pleaded guilty to misdemeanor federal charges that they inappropriately accessed the medical records of a local television anchor who was killed in 2008. Both physician and employees admitted to accessing the local celebrity's medical records for purely personal interest. Specifically, the physician admitted that after watching a news report regarding Ms. Pressly being slain and taken to St. Vincent's, where he was on staff, he logged on from home and accessed the hospital's records system to "determine if the news reports were accurate." One of the other charged employees, a former account representative at the hospital, admitted that she accessed Ms. Pressly's file about 12 times "out of curiosity." The third employee charged, an emergency room secretary, admitted that she "became curious about the patient's [Ms. Pressly's] status and accessed the medical chart to find out if the patient was still living."[5]

High Profile Early Settlement under HIPAA (pre-2013)

Harvard-Affiliated Hospital

On September 17, 2012, OCR announced a settlement agreement, including a $1.5 million CMP and a three-year corrective action and monitoring plan, with a Harvard Medical School teaching hospital, Massachusetts Eye and Ear Infirmary and Massachusetts Eye and Ear Associates, Inc. (MEEI).[6] The settlement came after the OCR investigated the theft of an unencrypted MEEI laptop that contained protected health information (PHI) of 3,500 individuals. OCR determined that MEEI demonstrated "a long-term, organizational disregard for the requirements of the [HIPAA] Security Rule," including failure to conduct a thorough analysis of risks associated with PHI on portable devices.

This settlement was notable for a number of reasons:

1. Prominence of the providers. MEEI is affiliated with Harvard Medical School, one of the most respected medical schools in the U.S. For them to be fined in this manner surely sends a message throughout the country.

2. The amount of the fine.

A $1.5 million fine to a non-profit academic institution also sent a message as to the importance of protecting PHI.

Recent Notable Cases and Enforcement Actions (2014+)

Byrne v. Avery Center for Obstetrics and Gynecology, P.C. (SC 18904)

In this 2014 Connecticut state case, the plaintiff (Byrne) began a personal relationship with an individual that ended after several months in 2004. Shortly after their relationship ended, the plaintiff advised Avery Center not to release her medical records to the individual. In May 2005, the individual instituted a paternity action against the plaintiff. In connection with the paternity action, Avery Center was served with a subpoena for the plaintiff's medical records. Avery Center did not alert the plaintiff of the subpoena, or file a motion to quash or appear in court; instead, it sent a copy of Byrne's medical file to the New Haven Regional Children's Probate Court. The plaintiff sued, alleging, among other claims, negligence in releasing the medical records. While the plaintiff lost at trial, the Connecticut Supreme Court reversed and remanded back to the trial court.

What was important in this case was that the state Supreme Court found that "HIPAA, and particularly its implementation through the Privacy Rule regulations, does not preempt causes of action, when they exist as a matter of state common or statutory law, arising from health care providers' breaches of confidentiality in a variety of contexts." Further the Court found that several other courts "....have determined that HIPAA may inform the relevant standard of care in such actions." Thus, a breach of the HIPAA Privacy Rule may serve as the underlying basis for a finding of a breach of a duty of care in a state court negligence action. This was a clear example that, while HIPAA does not offer a private cause of action for privacy violations, it does provide a standard against which a party's actions will be judged.

Enforcement Action and Settlement with Columbia NY Presbyterian Hospital

This 2014 enforcement action and settlement are notable due to the high profile of the violating hospital and university and because, at the time, it was the largest HIPAA settlement paid to date – a combined $4.8 million between the hospital and university.

The investigation found that the HIPAA data breach was caused when a physician employed by the university, who had developed applications for both the hospital and the university, "attempted to deactivate a personally owned computer server on the network." The breach caused exposure to the internet of more than 6,800 patients' records, including the patients' vital signs and lab test results.[7]

In addition to the financial penalties, each entity also agreed to prepare a "substantive corrective action plan" that included "undertaking a risk analysis, developing a risk management plan, revising policies and procedures, training staff and providing progress reports."

Emerging Class-Action Lawsuits vs. 21st Century Oncology

In perhaps the most interesting legal development in recent years, plaintiffs have begun to use a violation of the HIPPAA privacy standards to establish a case for negligence in handling their PHI. This was the essence of the Byrne case above. This trend sees its natural progression to this situation – multiple national class-action lawsuits against a covered entity for enormous exposure of patients' PHI.

In March 2016, just a few months before we updated the previous version of this monograph, 21st Century Oncology suffered a data breach that resulted in the exposure of over 2 million patients' PHI. The security breach, which was discovered by the FBI, exposed patients' Social Security numbers, health information, and insurance data.[8]

As of the date of publication of this 2019 edition, the class action lawsuit against 21st Century Oncology continues.[9]

Cases of Note Since Last Edition

Prominent Psychologist Suspended Because of Bill-Collection Methods

A New Jersey psychologist was sued by the state for HIPAA violations created by a billing practice. Here, the psychologist sent unpaid bills to a collections law firm, who then sued the patients for past due bills and, in the lawsuit filings, included patients' names, diagnoses and treatments. In the case, as of 2018, the state Board of Psychological Examiners upheld a decision by an administrative law judge that the psychologist pay fines and suffer a license suspension. The doctor was appealing and countersuing.[10]

This case is important because it shows that, ulitmately the physician and practice can be held responsible even for actions taken by outside firms working for them – here, the outside collections law firm. The doctor in this case was also counter-suing the collections law firm.

Wireless Health Service Provider Pays $2.5 Million Settlement Stemming from Stolen Employee Laptop

In January 2012, CardioNet reported to the HHS Office for Civil Rights (OCR) that a workforce member's laptop was stolen from a parked vehicle outside of the employee's home. The laptop contained the ePHI of 1,391 individuals. OCR's investigation into the impermissible disclosure revealed that CardioNet had an insufficient risk analysis and risk management processes in place at the time of the theft. Additionally, CardioNet's policies and procedures implementing the standards of the HIPAA Security Rule were in draft form and had not been implemented. Further, the organization was unable to produce any final policies or procedures regarding the implementation of safeguards for ePHI, including those for mobile devices.[11]

CardioNet and the OCR announced the settlement, which involved paying $2.5 million and implementing a corrective action plan, in April 2017.

This settlement is significant for a number of reasons: (1) it was the first OCR HIPAA settlement with a wireless healthcare provider; (2) the amount of the settlement was notable and, to the government, justified given the total lack of safeguards the company had implemented; and (3) the common nature of the breach – a stolen employee laptop, which is a risk that nearly every company and medical practice should consider and plan against.

Conclusion

In the first year or two after HIPAA became law, we saw a number of divergent trends developing. On one hand, the vast majority of claims brought under the law had been judged to be meritless by the agency tasked with enforcing the law, and the highest courts of the land confirmed that HIPAA did not afford a cause of action for a private lawsuit. On the other hand, courts began to use the HIPAA standards not only in actions brought strictly under its rules, but expanded HIPAA's potential reach by utilizing its rules as general standard of care in general tort/non-HIPAA related actions. Further, the justice department began to pursue criminal convictions or guilty pleas under the HIPAA statute itself.

These trends continued in more recent years. In the most recent enforcement actions noted above, we can also see that fines will be levied by the government where HIPAA violations occur, regardless of the reputation of the entity or even the size of a medical practice. Further, the trend of plaintiffs using the fact of a HIPPAA violation to make the case for a negligence action has only continued, even to the level of national class-action lawsuits and for actions of outside firms. We expect this trend to continue in the future.

Chapter 8
Self-Assessment Checklist

- Read the excellent list of HIPAA-related questions and answers on the American Medical Association's website at http://www.ama-assn.org/ama/pub/ physician-resources/solutions-managing-your- practice/coding-billing-insurance/hipaahealth- insurance-portability-accountability-act/frequently- asked-questions.shtml

- Work with a consultant or attorney experienced in HIPAA to review your practice's consent forms, procedures, and processes – to make sure they are compliant with this new and constantly-emerging area.

Chapter 8 – References

1. See http://www.hhs.gov/hipaa/for-professionals/compliance- enforcement/data/numbers-glance/index.html#allcomplaints.

2. See http://www.hhs.gov/hipaa/for-professionals/compliance- enforcement/data/enforcement-highlights/index.html.

3. https://www.hhs.gov/hipaa/for-professionals/compliance- enforcement/data/enforcement-highlights/index.html

4. See http://www.amednews.com/article/20080714/ government/307149978/6/

5. See https://hipaahealthlaw.foxrothschild.com/2009/07/articles/ hipaa-enforcement/dare-to-takeapeek-think-again/

6. http://www.hhs.gov/hipaa/for-professionals/compliance- enforcement/examples/MEEI/

7. Conn, Joseph. "New York-Presbyterian, Columbia to pay largest HIPAA settlement: $4.8 million," *Modern Healthcare*. May 7, 2014. See http://www.modernhealthcare.com/ article/20140507/NEWS/305079946 .

8. See http://www.hipaajournal.com/21st-century-oncology- patients-seek-damages-after-phi-exposure-3371/.

9. See https://www.krcomplexlit.com/currentcases/21st- century-oncology-data-breach/.

10. https://www.propublica.org/article/barry-helfmann-psychologist-license-suspension-new-jersey

11. https://www.hhs.gov/about/news/2017/04/24/2-5-million-settlement-shows-not-understanding-hipaa-requirements-creates-risk.html

Method of Participation for Obtaining CME Credit for Chapters 7 and 8

There are no fees to receive CME credit for participating in this activity. If you wish to receive continuing education credit, please do the following:

1. Review the objectives, statement of need, and disclosure information.

2. Read the indicated chapters.

3. To obtain the maximum benefit from this activity, you are encouraged to complete the self-assessment checklist at the end of each chapter, as applicable, and formulate an action plan based on each self-assessment exercise.

4. Go online using the URL below and complete the self-assessment (achieving a passing score of 70 percent) and the activity evaluation. If you do not achieve a passing score in three attempts, please contact CEServices@cme.com to have your account reset. Upon passing the assessment and completing the evaluation, you will be able to print or save your certificate of credit.

www.academycme.org/actID=19GU164
activity code: 19GU164

Nonmedical Liability Risks for the Practicing Physician

Most physicians spend much of their time concerned about (and, ideally, working to prevent) medical malpractice claims. Although this concern is certainly justified, what many do not realize is that the every-day risks common to any operating business can also be a source of considerable liability. Like any small business owner, the practicing physician must endure the "triple threat of business liability."

This "triple threat" consists of the following: (1) lawsuits from your employees (age, race, or gender discrimination; sexual harassment; or wrongful termination); (2) lawsuits brought against your employees or partners for harassment, injury, or even violation of consumer collection laws; and (3) claims brought by patients and other visitors to your practice due to personal injuries occurring on premises or involving practice equipment and vehicles.

Reducing Liability to Your Employees and Staff

These days are treacherous for employee lawsuits. With Congress and state legislatures expanding the rights of employees, juries handing out excessive awards as a matter of routine, and unscrupulous lawyers feeding the litigation fire, employers have good reason to be worried. More employees will sue their bosses in the next decade than did workers in the past three decades combined! And physicians are no exception to this trend.

Sexual harassment, race discrimination, wrongful termination, violation of the Americans with Disabilities Act, age discrimination, running afoul of federal Medicare fraud provisions, HIPAA, gender discrimination, EEOC violations, breach-of-employment contract, and mismanagement of a staff pension fund can all be grounds for a potentially devastating lawsuit. Although this is beyond the scope of this monograph, we implore you to find out more about employee lawsuits and how to avoid them through proper human resources policies.

Reducing Liability of Your Employees and Staff

The behavior of employees and staff can be time bombs ticking away in your office. Without proper employee policies, these time bombs could explode with possibly ruinous results both in terms of patient care and in lawsuit liability.

Under the law, you, your practice, and your partners can be held legally and financially responsible for the behavior of your employees. Further, even if staff members are not your employees, you may be held responsible if they acted under your direction in a clinic or hospital. More important, patients will include their judgment of your staff in how they evaluate your medical care (and whether or not they recommend you to others in person or online). For these reasons, it is essential that you institute policies that minimize the risk of staff misbehavior.

- **The Unqualified Employee Who Gives Medical Advice**
  One family practitioner was recently sued when one of her receptionists told a patient to take Anacin instead of aspirin, not realizing that Anacin contains aspirin. The patient, who was already taking an anticoagulant, developed gastrointestinal bleeding and was later admitted to the hospital. She also ended up suing the physician for malpractice.

    Unfortunately, this type of situation occurs quite often. Assistants who hear common complaints from patients take notice of the diagnoses and treatments prescribed by their physician-bosses. In an effort to "not waste the doctor's time" on routine questions, these assistants sometimes will make quick recommendations to patients. Although these recommendations may be harmless and correct advice most of the time, whenever there is a problem (either due to wrong advice or a misinterpretation of the advice by the patient), you, as the physician, will be held responsible.

Recommendation

Make sure your nonmedical staff members never give medical advice under any circumstances. Be clear in your policy/employee manual, and make sure your employees understand.

- **The Employee Who Files Reports Before You've Read Them**

  Even when modern information management systems are put into place in medical offices, it is the staff that must make the system work. Often staffers are too eager to get all reports filed, forgetting that the physician must see the reports to ensure proper patient care and follow-up. Take heed from the following case:

Case Study

Dr. W sent their patient Pete for a full range of laboratory work and a chest x-ray film as part of his physical examination. All the laboratory tests came back negative a few days later, and Dr. W had an assistant call Pete to give him the news. A second office assistant filed the x-ray film report, which came in two days after the laboratory reports. The x-ray film indicated a probable malignancy in the right lung. The x-ray report was not shown to Dr. W but instead was filed so Dr. W would see it at the follow-up appointment.

There was no follow-up appointment. Pete thought that when all the tests were negative, he did not need to come back into the office. It was not until a year later, when

Dr. W was served with a court summons, that he opened Pete's file and saw the x-ray film report. Meanwhile, Pete had been diagnosed with metastatic lung cancer and was suing Dr. W for missing the diagnosis.

As this case indicates, the mishandling of information — test results or other — can be extremely hazardous. Investigate how your support staff would have handled this situation. Could the mishap that occurred in Dr. W's office take place in yours? Do you have a rule or procedure that ensures that this mistake is avoided?

Recommendation
Establish this simple rule for all employees: Never have them file any piece of information — even if they are "sure" the doctor will see it prior to the patient's next visit — if it does not have the physician's initials on it.

- **The Staffer Who Fails to Document Patient Contacts**
  Over the years, in part because of the emergence of risk management teachings, physicians have become better at documenting their communications with patients. We have emphasized the point repeatedly in this monograph. However, documentation is just as important for medical office employees. As we have stressed, chart notes of all patient contacts not only improve patient care (by preserving valuable knowledge about the patient's history), but also serve an invaluable service if your care is ever called into question later, in a malpractice suit or otherwise.

Recommendation
Make sure that staffers understand that every patient contact should be recorded in the patient's records. Yellow stick-on notes will not do, as they fall off too easily. All the information from each contact should end up in the file every time. Allow no exceptions.

Reducing Liability From
The Medical Office Premises

Here, the third element of the "triple threat" will be examined: lawsuit dangers emerging from the medical office premises; that is, "premises liability." Although the discussion will be focused primarily on lawsuits brought by patients and other visitors to your medical office, these problems are also common sources of claims by employees in the form of lawsuits or workers' compensation claims. Thus, by following the recommended strategies, you can not only lower your exposure to outside lawsuits, but reduce your costs of workers' compensation or insurance premiums as well.

NOTE: Do not think, because the terms "property owner" and "landowner" are used here, that you are not at risk because you lease or otherwise rent your office premises. The law imposes premises liability on persons who lease property as it does for property owners.

The Legal Test

Like any other public accommodation, your office must be a "reasonably safe" premises "under the circumstances." What is "reasonable" under any set of circumstances, of course, is open to interpretation and argument. Although no physician (or any other property owner, for that matter) has the absolute duty to ensure the safety of his guests, he cannot ignore the issue entirely. In fact, the duty of care required of property owners varies with the circumstances, so it is often difficult to determine just how much attention to premises is enough.

In the end, the question of whether or not you are found to be liable for any injury at your office will center on four questions: What type of hazard caused the injury in question? How obvious was the hazard? How long had it existed before actions (if any) to prevent injury were taken? Were the precautions reasonable under the circumstances?

Once again, we are faced with the "reasonable under the circumstances" language: the type of gray area that frustrates nonlawyers and gives fodder to both sides of any legal debate. As physicians, we are particularly vulnerable to this inquiry because the guests on our premises are often persons most susceptible to injury: children, the infirm, the elderly. As such, we will be held to an extraordinarily high standard of care. What are reasonable precautions for many business owners may be inadequate in our circumstances.

The Scope of the Threat

In a 1991 closed-case study performed by the Risk Management Foundation (RMF) of the Harvard Medical Institutions, Inc. delved into premises-based liability for practices. Although the study is older, it is still quite instructive. In this study fully 15 percent of all claims managed by the foundation over a 14-year period were cases involving patient falls.[1] Although the majority of these cases accounted for relatively minor losses, the growth of large-verdict slip-and-fall cases in recent years indicate that the costs associated with patient falls can be significant. Fall-related claims can put a strain on valuable time and resources that are needed to address other more severe risk areas.

The Harvard RMF study also demonstrated a number of trends associated with medical office slip-and-fall cases, including the following high-risk factors:[2]

1. A patient older than 65 years

2. A patient with altered mental status

3. Substances on the office floor

4. Malfunctioning equipment

5. Assistance with mobility by a member of the staff

Further, the Harvard RMF study found that injuries occurred most often in the following areas (in order of frequency):[3]

1. Patient's room

2. Halls and lobbies

3. Patient's bathroom

4. Radiology examination area

5. Emergency treatment areas

Do you see the high-risk factors and high-frequency injury areas in your practice? If you do, you are especially at risk for slip-and-fall lawsuits. Even if you do not, the premises liability danger is still an important risk to guard against, especially when you can reduce much of your risk by simply paying attention to a small number of potentially hazardous areas.

"Walking Around Knowledge" Required

The most important step you can take to reduce your premises liability risk is to gain some "walking around" knowledge of your office: that is making inspections of your office at regular intervals. These inspections should be made by you and your staff as well. In fact, all physicians and staff should make regular inspection of key patient areas, making notes for potential hazards. By simply making inspections part of your operational routine, you will do much to highlight potential problems before they become hazardous.

Beyond this general rule, there are a number of key areas that are potential hazards in any office. The following list highlights the most important risk areas and suggests ways to improve safety and reduce the chance of a slip and fall injury and lawsuit.

Access

Challenge

Patients should be able to negotiate the office and its surroundings easily and safely. A slip/fall in the entrance of the office is one of the most common liability-producing scenarios. The usual culprits are slippery floors, carpet in disrepair, or faulty doors.

Recommendation

Walkways should be level and in good repair, doors should open easily, and stairwells should have adequate handrails. Always check carpets for disrepair or floors for wet areas. Nonskid matting is always a wise idea in office entrances, especially in areas of the country where wet or snowy weather is common.

Many potential hazards, such as wet floors, should be corrected immediately in order to avoid liability. The inquiry of how soon the landowner acted to prevent injury is one of the questions asked in the legal test for liability. Office staff should be trained not only to make routine inspections of the entrance and other high-risk areas, but also to order or make easy repairs immediately. There is nothing that juries and judges look down upon more than the situation in which the landowner sees one person injured by a hazard and does nothing before a second person is also injured by the same hazard.

The importance of using of signs to warn patients of potential hazards cannot be overstated. Here, this may mean "slippery when wet" and "wet floor" signs and other portable barriers to redirect traffic away from hazardous areas. In other areas, this may mean "Staff Only: No Admittance" signs or even cones and tape to block off restricted areas. In short, the investment you make in warning signs and portable barriers will pay for itself many times over in prevented injuries and claims.

Medical Equipment and Biohazardous Waste

Challenge
Consider the following hypothetical case study involving equipment and waste:

Case Study

In your medical office laboratory, the young son of one of your female patients was left unattended while the phlebotomist drew the patient's blood. The child, meanwhile, had climbed quietly up onto the counter and began reaching for the bright red sharps container. Before long, the boy got to the container and began playing with the needles. While the phlebotomist soon realized what was going on, and rushed the boy away from the container, it could have been too late.

In this case study, if the child was infected with HIV, hepatitis, or any other communicable disease, your liability could be enormous. This case study also demonstrates not only the importance of monitoring children in your office (discussed later), but also the need for safeguards around dangerous medical equipment and materials.

Recommendation
Biohazardous waste cannot be stored in patient-care areas or other high-traffic sites. Further, waste containers used in examination and treatment rooms must be secured to prevent spillage and keep out inquisitive patients and guests. If gas cylinders are used in the office, they should be stored and secured properly. Electrical equipment should be inspected regularly and should never be used when not functioning properly. Sharps, medications, and other potentially hazardous materials should be stored away from patients' access and locked away, if appropriate.

Driveways and Parking Lots
Challenge
Although cases have held that driveways and parking lots are not inherently dangerous areas, physicians are still routinely held responsible when patients are injured in their parking lots. Consider the case in which a woman entered a physician's office to make a phone call for emergency car service. She was not even a patient. When the woman left the office, walking through the doctor's lot, she was hit by a car. Allegedly, the car was driven by a patient, although no one stopped, and the driver was never identified. The injured woman sued the doctor, and the physician's comprehensive liability policy ultimately paid on the claim.

Recommendation
Driveways should be well marked with arrows and signs. The views in the lot should be unobstructed by landscaping. One-way traffic flow is also a wise idea, as are speed bumps or dips.

Children
Challenge
Injuries to children are an ever-increasing source of lawsuits against landowners of all types. As the case study showed, you must be concerned with injuries to children, especially if you often have children as patients or in your waiting rooms. General practitioners, pediatricians, and gynecologists are most severely at risk.

The most common type of claim brought on behalf of children is the typical injury due to an accident that causes fracture or lacerations. However, injuries can be severe (electrocution, paralyzation).

Recommendation

Maintain the office as explained above; child-proof the office (covering electric outlets, using child-proof locks on closets, etc.); train staff to be particularly aware of children's whereabouts and behavior; and use signs and warnings to alert adults that they, not you, are responsible for their children's behavior and/or injuries. A "play at your own risk" sign is always a good idea.

Bathroom

Challenge

Bathrooms are a common source of liability, especially for physicians with elderly patients. The two major liability factors for injuries occurring in bathrooms are design and maintenance. Although maintenance of a safe bathroom is fairly straightforward, consider the problem of a faulty bathroom design:

An internist-lessee of a renovated facility found that serious errors had been made in bathroom design. Doors opened inward, and the rooms themselves were so small that, if a patient collapsed on the floor, entry by another person would have been barred. Further there were no emergency bells to alert staff if a patient fell or was otherwise immobilized in the rooms.

Recommendation

Design bathrooms with the knowledge that sick and incapacitated people will be using them. If you are moving into a new facility, investigate the bathrooms with these concerns in mind. If you already have a facility with inadequate bathrooms, you should, at the very least, install emergency bells and regularly inspect and maintain the rooms. Finally, if feasible, attempt a low-cost renovation to improve the bathroom's layout.

Throughout this chapter, we have discussed ways to reduce the chance that you will be sued by concerning yourself with the physical structure of your office. However, an equally important issue is how to discourage lawsuits by using the proper legal structure for your practice. By using professional corporations, limited liability companies, limited partnerships, and even trusts in certain situations, you can effectively discourage lawsuits before they become financially and emotionally draining.

Chapter 9
Self-Assessment Guide

- **Liabilities to employees and staff**
  Do you have an employee manual that outlines all policies regarding discrimination, harassment, etc.?

  Has a labor lawyer familiar with your state rules on employment, as well as federal guidelines, reviewed your policies and mandatory postings in your office?

- **Liabilities because of staff or employees**
  Have you made clear in employment contracts, manuals, or other policy statements that you will not allow nonmedical staff to dispense medical advice? Are there repercussions if an employee fails to follow this rule?

  Have you made clear in employment contracts, manuals, or other policy statements all reports should be seen by the physicians before filing? Do you have some type of initial or check-off system?

  Have you made clear in employment contracts, manuals, or other policy statements that all patient contacts should be noted in patients' charts?

- **Liabilities from the medical office premises**
  The form on the following page can be used as a basis for inspection of your office premises.

Chapter 9 – References

1. Analysis of slip/fall related claims at the Harvard Medical Institutions. *Forum*. 1991; 12(1):2-5.

2. Analysis of slip/fall related claims at the Harvard Medical Institutions. *Forum*. 1991; 12(1):2-5.

3. Analysis of slip/fall related claims at the Harvard Medical Institutions. *Forum*. 1991; 12(1):2-5.

OFFICE PREMISES CHECKLIST

Driveway and parking lot are well-marked, with arrows, and signs. Views in the lot are unobstructed by signs and/or landscaping.
Yes ___ No ___
Comment
_____

Stairwell leading to entrance is in good repair, clear of debris, free of ice or is salted, and has adequate railing.
Yes ___ No ___
Comment
_____

Entrance is handicapped-accessible and ramp is also free of debris and ice.
Yes ___ No ___
Comment
_____

Front door and other doors open easily and leave room for pedestrian traffic (and gurneys, if applicable).
Yes ___ No ___
Comment
_____

Other stairwells are in good repair, free from debris, and have adequate railing.
Yes ___ No ___
Comment
_____

All walkways, including hallways, are in good repair (no carpeting sticking up) and are level.
Yes ___ No ___
Comment
_____

All wet areas are covered by nonskid matting and are clearly denoted by signs and/or isolated by protective barriers.
Yes ___ No ___
Comment
_____

All biohazardous waste is stored away from patient areas or high-traffic staff areas.
Yes ___ No ___
Comment
_____

All waste containers used in examination rooms are secure.
Yes ___ No ___
Comment
_____

All electrical equipment is in proper working order.
Yes ___ No ___
Comment
_____

All sharps, medications, and other potentially hazardous materials are stored away from patients' access and/or locked.
Yes ___ No ____
Comment

_____

Bathrooms are dry, not slippery, and are in a good state of repair (and have emergency bells, if applicable).
Yes ___ No ____
Comment

_____

Office has been childproofed (ie, electric outlets are covered, childproof locks are installed on closets, signs have been installed warning adults of their responsibility of their children).
Yes ___ No ____
Comment

_____

Inspection performed by _____

Date of inspection _____

Risk Management Regarding Today's Technologies and Telemedicine

One of the fastest-growing developments in risk management involves telemedicine. This should not come as a surprise, given the increasing reliance on technology, especially the internet and wireless communication, in virtually every other field of endeavor. While the advances in telemedicine may be beneficial for patient and physician alike, they also create new risks that need to be better understood and properly managed.

When we use the term "telemedicine" here, we will cover two distinct concepts. One is the delivery of healthcare services through the emerging technologies. In some specialties, such as radiology, telemedicine is quite robust already, going into its second decade of relevance. Regarding this area, we will continue the discussion we began in the prior version of the monograph below.

Before we get to that analysis, however, we will first cover an area that likely impacts every physician practicing today: how to use (and not use) everyday technologies in a medical practice environment, from texting, emailing and social media, to what to do about online reviews.

Texting

Texting has become ubiquitous in recent years as a way for people to communicate quickly and efficiently and, for physicians and other healthcare professionals, this is no different. In fact, as far back at 2012, an article cited a study which showed that 73 percent of physicians texted other physicians about work.[1]

More recent studies show an increased use of the technology. In fact, a 2018 study of 770 hospital professionals and 1,279 physician practices demonstrated that 85% of hospitals and 83% of physician practices were using secure communication platforms between care teams, patients, and families.[2]

Not surprisingly, however, the most concerning element from a risk management perspective, is the texting of PHI which triggers the protections of HIPPAA. The most significant of such texting risks include:

1. Text messages may reside on a mobile device indefinitely, and thus could be accessed if the device is ever lost, stolen or recycled.

2. Text messages are typically accessible with little, if any, authentication.

3. Text messages are often not monitored by the IT department.

Given that encryption technology has become readily accessible and available, it is difficult to take the position, even for small practices, that it is not reasonable and appropriate. In short, unless there is a very good reason not to, providers should encrypt electronic PHI in all circumstances, including texting.

In addition to using encryption technology, the American Bar Association (ABA)'s health law group has published this excellent checklist of precautions to consider when it comes to texting in healthcare:

- Encrypt all mobile devices that are used to transmit clinical information.

- Ensure that texts are sent over a secure platform provided by a vendor who understands its obligations as a business associate under the HIPAA Security Rule as well as the practical parameters for designing the platform to be compliant with all HIPAA Security Rule requirements.

- Double up - require a username and password to use the secure platform.

- Do not allow the texting of any practitioner orders at this time.

- Adopt a remote wiping system that can be used should the mobile device holding clinical texts be lost or stolen.

- Specify a process for all employees/workforce members to immediately notify the entity's Security Officer of lost or stolen mobile devices.

- Do not allow concurrent personal use of devices that are used to text clinical information. In other words, separate devices should be used for work and for personal purposes.

- Adopt a robust, complete texting policy that incorporates these suggestions and addresses all of the risks identified above before allowing any texting of clinical information.

- Train all workforce on the texting policy and enforce it rigorously[3]

Email

Like texting, since the 2016 edition, email has only become a larger part of everyone's lives – and healthcare is no exception to this trend. Also, as with texting, the central risk to be managed regards the protection of patients' ePHI. State privacy laws and, of course, HIPAA are impacted with email, like they are with texting.

As we write this 2019 edition, an excellent two-part article on providers' use of email and its HIPAA implications was published by the Fox Group.[4] In this article, the authors succinctly describe how HIPAA impacts email, addressing healthcare providers:

- Email communications are permitted, but you must take precautions;

- It is a good idea to warn patients about the risks of using email that includes patient health information (PHI);

- Providers should be prepared to use email for certain communications, if requested by the patient, but must ensure they are not exposing information the patient does not want to be shared; and

- Providers must take steps to protect the integrity of information and protect information shared over open networks.[5]

In part two of the article, the authors give five recommendations on being HIPAA-compliant with email:

1. **Be the expert on the topic of HIPAA compliant email on behalf of your patients.** This means making sure you have appropriate notices visible, both online and in the real world, warning patients about the potential security risks of transmitting protected health information (PHI) using email over the non-secure portion of the Internet.

2. **Document the patient's consent to receive communication by email.** Don't assume that because your patient sent an email requesting PHI or sharing PHI, that he or she understands the risks of sending or receiving such emails. Consider using a form that the patient signs allowing such email use.

3. **Use an EHR system with a patient portal function.** If you're using an EHR system with a patient portal function, encourage patients to use the portal's capabilities for secure communications. Most portals utilize secure channels for the information available via the portal, but make sure the vendor certifies that to you – and then test it yourself prior to encouraging patients to use it.

4. **Consider signing up for a secure, HIPAA-compliant email application.** If you must use email to communicate with patients, a secure email application will protect your communications by using secure channels to send those emails.

5. **Manually encrypt transmitted files.** If you don't have a patient portal and don't want to use a secure, HIPAA-compliant email application, avoid including PHI in the text of email, and encrypt any files containing PHI that you are sending to patients.[6]

Social Media

As with texting, since our last edition of this monograph, the use of social media by physicians has skyrocketed. Social media has been primarily used as a method for physicians to provide information and even communicate with patients and prospective patients. This also brings with it a different set of risks.

A short list of behaviors to consider when engaging in social media:

1. Be sure not to expose protected health information (PHI). The casual nature of social media sometimes causes physicians and staff to let their guard down and make costly mistakes, such as inadvertently exposing PHI on their social media pages. Per earlier chapters, this can create potential governmental fines and civil liability to injured plaintiffs as well.

2. Do not cross professional boundaries. Again, because of the social media environment, physicians may cross professional boundaries in their comments in a way that they would never do in an in-person environment. This needs to be consciously avoided.

3. Be clear not to create a treatment relationship. When physicians have an online presence, individuals sometimes ask them treatment related questions online. If physicians answer such questions, this can be problematic.

4. Understand that all activity is discoverable. All social media activity (on behalf of the practice, its physicians, and its staff) is potentially discoverable should a lawsuit arise.[7]

Online Reviews

Like texting and social media, online reviews have become a fact of life in today's world of medicine, no matter how unwanted. Any online search of a physician will inevitably have multiple online review sites come up on the first page of the search, often before the physician's own practice page or the listing from the hospital/healthcare system. Zocdoc, healthgrades, vitals, and doximity are a few of the popular sites. Even larger players like webMD have also gotten in this business.

The greatest risk management issue regarding online reviews deals with what to do – and what not to do – when you see negative reviews. With an increasing number of such reviews finding their way onto such sites, many business and communication consultants have included counseling physicians on such issues as part of their services. An excellent article on the subject listed more than actions to take (or not take). We have highlighted them here:[8]

1. **Do not respond right away.** The goal is to be calm and respectful in your reply, not to start an online shouting match. In fact, you may find, that after some time, you choose not to respond at all.

2. **Consider the patient's perspective.** Some negative reviews may be less about you than a bad situation the patient was going through. Other comments might be valid complaints about your practice. Could you or your staff have prevented the situation? Is this a common complaint, something you have heard multiple times? If so, this negative feedback could actually be helpful to you to improve your services.

3. **Don't ask the patient to take their review down.** It is bad practice to ask the reviewer to take their comments down. Instead, focus on addressing their complaint and resolving any problems. If you're lucky, the patient will appreciate your effort and consider changing or updating their review on their own.

4. **If the review is obviously fake, try contacting the review site.** If the negative review in question is

obviously fake, or not about you or your practice, contact the review site and provide your evidence. Review sites don't like fake reviews either.

5. **Protect patient confidentiality.** Per above, you cannot reference any PHI when replying back publicly to the review, if you choose to respond. Evaluate whether to respond publicly or privately. If the patient's complaint was about your medical advice, you won't be able to respond publicly without breaking confidentiality. However, comments about customer service, office decor, and wait times are all fair game.

6. **Don't be defensive.** A defensive response won't do anyone any good. Don't argue with the reviewer or try to justify your side. Instead, acknowledge the reader's trouble and show concern that they didn't have a positive experience. Address legitimate complaints and correct any inaccurate information in a polite way by talking about your standard procedures.

7. **Thank the reviewer.** This is the number one thing to remember: Negative feedback can improve your practice. Although you might not be happy about receiving black marks, an online review site can be a good source of honest patient feedback. Don't you want to know if your patients are dissatisfied? Thank the reviewer for taking the time to give their opinion and let them know they are helping you improve your practice.

8. **Stay up-to-date with online review sites.** If you check online review sites regularly, you will have the chance to respond to negative reviews in a timely manner. A quick reply will show your commitment to online engagement and may even allow you to catch and resolve a patient's problem.

9. **Take the opportunity to build your own profile on the major review sites,** such as Healthgrades.com,

Vitals.com and RateMDs.com, and start to reframe
your practice's online image.

10. **Ask patients to post their opinions online.** One
negative online review isn't going to damage your
reputation. However, if your entire online presence
is a few negative reviews, they could skew your
practice image. Try asking more of your patients to
write online reviews.[9]

What is Telemedicine?

Before we examine the risks created by "telemedicine," we need
to define this term. The American Medical Association has defined
telemedicine as "medical practice across distance via electronic
communications system and interactive video technology." While
a layperson might ask what types of medicine can actually be practiced "virtually" under the AMA's definition, physicians understand better.

With its focus on diagnostics, where physicians read studies
that can be transported easily via internet or even wireless technology, radiology is the field in which telemedicine has grown most
significantly.

Example: Teleradiology

Sending radiology information from one point to another (i.e. from
the hospital to the radiologist's home, from one medical facility
to another, etc.) has been practiced for 15 years. A system that
moves radiology images and stores them is known as a PACS (Pic-
ture Archiving and Communication System), and the system that
handles the patient demographic, clinical and financial information
is known as RIS (Radiology Information System). In the last seven
years, a large industry has been created using RIS/PACS technology
to deliver hospital emergency scans to radiologists in the U.S. and
overseas to cover hospitals throughout the night.

Case Study: Teleradiology

On a cold and misty night in November, Joan, a retired

secretary, was walking across a dark parking lot outside a restaurant. She suddenly slipped and fell heavily on her right arm and shoulder. Experiencing severe pain in the arm, she suspected she might be hurt and she hailed a cab to a local hospital emergency room. The triage nurse examined Joan very briefly, took a quick history, and told her to wait to be seen by the doctor.

Three hours later Joan was finally seen by Dr Andrews, the emergency room physician. Her elbow and upper arm were bruised, there was swelling around the elbow and she had a great difficulty in rotating her forearm. Her shoulder and hip were hurting, and there was some bruising over her hip. The physician ordered x-rays of her shoulder, hip and elbow, and Joan was brought to radiology about 12:30 AM to have all studies performed.

Joan did not realize that her x-rays were not going to be read by a radiologist in the hospital, but rather they were being transmitted overseas by the internet. The hospital had recently contracted with an overseas reading service that covered the hospital's radiology reading each night from 11PM to 7AM. This service utilized American-trained radiologists who were licensed in several states. This hospital contract was a new one for this service, and the first one in Joan's state. Through a scheduling oversight, the radiologist reading Joan's films was licensed in the U.S., but not in the state in which the hospital was located.

Within 45 minutes, the radiologist reported Joan's case back to the ER. He reported seeing no fracture, but did comment that the films were of limited technical quality, and that repeat films and additional views should be obtained depending on the patient's clinical presentation. The busy ER physician obtained the negative report from the secretary who received the faxed report. He did not order any additional films, and discharged Joan home with ice packs and instructions to see her internist the next day.

At 9:00 the following morning, Dr. Smith, one of the hospital radiologists, reviewed Joan's films. He found that the three fractures around the elbow that he recognized had not been reported by the teleradiology service. He immediately called the ER, and spoke with the attending physician for the day, as Dr. Andrews had gone off shift and was no longer in the hospital. Dr. Smith transmitted his concern that with the fractures and dislocation he saw, the patient could suffer nerve damage if untreated.

The ER physician put in place the hospital's call back policy for its ER patients, and within twenty minutes Joan was being told that she must return to the hospital for further treatment. This time there was no delay when she entered the emergency room. An orthopedic surgeon met her shortly after she arrived and his assessment confirmed the fears of the radiologist that Joan had suffered nerve impairment. He took her to the OR, reduced the fractures and dislocation, but the nerve damage remained. Joan would never again regain total use of that arm.

Within a day, the director of risk management at the hospital had been notified and was investigating this case. What she found out did not please her. After notifying the hospital malpractice insurer, she discovered that her state required that any institution using out of hospital facilities to provide care was obligated to notify its patients of that policy. Not only was the risk management director unaware of this policy, she discovered that the rest of the staff were also uninformed. She realized that doctors providing care to hospital patients must be licensed in her state, but not until later did she discover that this was not true in Joan's case. Finally, to her dismay, she found out that the hospital had not even followed its own policy of credentialing physicians when it came to contracting with the nightcall radiology provider. None of the teleradiology physicians were even listed on the hospital staff.

The director then did a more thorough investigation of the teleradiology contract. She found there were no requirements for HIPAA certification in the contract, and that quality issues regarding film resolution were not addressed. There wasn't even a clear hospital privacy policy included in the contract. When she asked for a copy of the insurance policy covering this contract, she discovered that the limits of liability the hospital required were present, but that there were aggregate limits applying to all 22 of the radiologists reading for this group, not for any one radiologist. Furthermore, she found out that two other cases were pending against the group, and that by the time they got to her case, the insurance limits might be met.

This case illustrates many of the potential problems associated with telemedicine practice, and it is a very possible scenario in any facility. While the results in this case were severe for Joan, many cases occur daily with minimal negative results but with the same risk factors present.

Telemedicine and the Doctor-Patient Relationship

In our last edition of this monograph, we wrote that the traditional physician-patient relationship with face-to-face consultations is now potentially complicated by communication technology. By potentially adding emotional as well as physical distance between physician and patient, technology may actually alter that essential relationship. Interpreting an extremely helpful article by healthcare attorneys Tara Kepler and Charlene L. McGinty, we noted that the authors recognized that the boundaries of the physician-patient relationship created by these virtual encounters are not yet well established in case law.

At that time, the attorneys noted that courts have reviewed other indirect encounters and have developed applicable guidelines for determining whether a physician-patient relationship has been formed pursuant to a remote telemedicine encounter. These courts have used the following types of guidelines for determining if a physician-patient relationship existed:

- A physician-patient relationship may exist even though the physician and patient have never had direct contact;

- A physician-patient relationship may exist where others have contracted with the physician on the patient's behalf;

- A physician-patient relationship exists if the relationship was contracted for or with the express or implied consent of the patient or for the patient's benefit; and

- A physician-patient relationship exists when healthcare services are rendered on behalf of the patient and are done for the patient's benefit.[10]

To assist its membership, the American Medical Association (AMA), within its Advocacy Resource Center, has published an online 50-state survey of the various rules that govern the establishment of a patient-physician relationship via telemedicine. See https://www.ama-assn.org/system/files/2018-10/ama-chart-telemedicine-patient-physician-relationship.pdf. This can be a good first resource for physicians, but nothing should replace a consult with an experienced attorney in the field.

Getting Advice is Critical

This area, like all areas related to technology, is changing rapidly due to constantly emerging state and federal legislation, new cases in the courts, and medical self-regulatory standards. Further, given the comments above and the references to the leading article by the healthcare attorneys referenced above, this is a complex area of risk management. Therefore, it is critical that if you want advice in this area, you consult a healthcare attorney, risk management consultant, or other local professional who works in this area.

Chapter 10
Self-Assessment Checklist

Texting and Social Media

Per our discussion above, with regard to texting, consider the ABA's recommendations:

- Encrypt all mobile devices that are used to transmit clinical information.

- Ensure that texts are sent over a secure platform provided by a vendor who understands its obligations as a business associate under the HIPAA Security Rule as well as the practical parameters for designing the platform to be compliant with all HIPAA Security Rule requirements.

- Double up - require a username and password to use the secure platform.

- Do not allow the texting of any practitioner orders at this time.

- Adopt a remote wiping system that can be used should the mobile device holding clinical texts be lost or stolen.

- Specify a process for all employees/workforce members to immediately notify the entity's Security Officer of lost or stolen mobile devices.

- Do not allow concurrent personal use of devices that are used to text clinical information. In other words, separate devices should be used for work and for personal purposes.

- Adopt a robust, complete texting policy that incorporates these suggestions and addresses all of the risks identified above before allowing any texting of clinical information.

- Train all workforce on the texting policy and enforce it rigorously.[11]

Per our discussion above, with regard to social media:

1. **Be sure not to expose protected health information (PHI).** The casual nature of social media sometimes causes physicians and staff to let their guard down and make costly mistakes, such as inadvertently exposing PHI on their social media pages. Per earlier chapters, this can create potential governmental fines and civil liability to injured plaintiffs as well.

2. **Do not cross professional boundaries.** Again, because of the social media environment, physicians may cross professional boundaries in their comments in a way that they would never consider to do so in an in-person environment. This needs to be consciously avoided.

3. **Be clear not to create a treatment relationship.** When physicians have an online presence, individuals sometimes ask them treatment related questions online. If physicians answer such questions, this can be problematic.

4. **Understand that all activity is discoverable.** All social media activity (on behalf of the practice, its physicians, and its staff) is potentially discoverable should a lawsuit arise.

Telemedicine

As above, *there is no substitute here for an attorney/consultant with in-depth knowledge of this field of risk management specifically in the area of telemedicine.* Nevertheless, we have attempted to pick out common advice from our research. Please see the checklist below for this "common sense" advice – much of it coming from a particular well-respected consultant in the field. Although their advice is twenty years old, much of it still rings true today:[12]

- Read and understand your state laws regarding telemedicine liability. Consult with an attorney if you need help here. Subscribe to publications to keep yourself current on these and other laws passed in your state. At the time of this writing, nearly one half of the states have a policy and reimbursement for telemedicine.

- Weigh the advantages and disadvantages of becoming licensed and credentialed in all states for which you intend to provide telemedicine services. Some states have specific "telemedicine licenses" but most require full licensure in that state to practice at all, regardless of the method.

- Obtain professional liability insurance coverage for the specific duties you are performing in telemedicine; understand the limits of your liability for telemedicine practice, and obtain the details of coverage as well as limits of your liability for telemedicine practice from your specific carrier. Obtain a written agreement from your carrier regarding their coverage of your specific program and its specific services. Do not settle for written agreements or "form" letters that don't specify your program and its services.

- Provide patients with written lists of alternatives and behavioral suggestions in the case of equipment failure, accident or catastrophe. Have a backup plan that includes referrals to local practitioners in your specialty if necessary, should the internet or other communication system you rely on fail for any reason.

- When delivering innovative service in an area where validated research has not yet been established, fully inform all clients both verbally and in writing of such practice as being outside the standard, and in an area not yet validated by research. In the consent form, include issues such as advantages and limitations of telemedicine service delivery, including inherent deficiencies in the electronic equipment possibly interfering with diagnosis or treatment; issues related to equipment failure; choice of venue waivers to resolve issues of jurisdiction; a brief description of equipment and services to be delivered; and the purpose, benefits, potential risks and other consequences of services delivered. Describe the specific roles of the consultant and local referring practitioner, including which one has ultimate authority over the patient's treatment, and state that the information will be stored in a computerized data base.

- Be sure to inform patients of practitioner licensure, and provide state licensing board contact information. Collect patient satisfaction measures regularly throughout service delivery. Arrange for proper scanning and sharing of release forms signed by patients so that local practitioner, remote consultants and patients themselves can have copies for their files.

- Be certain that your staff is following whatever standards of care might exist in telemedicine for your program specialty area. Check with your professional associations for their statements regarding telemedicine practice, research, or education. This may include technical requirements of the sending and viewing technology as in specialties of radiology, cardiology, dermatology, pathology.

- Seek vendors willing and able to provide:
  1. support 24/7 to train new staff and patients, as well as avoid errors leading to data destruction.

  2. downtime instructions for accessing emergency information during scheduled and unscheduled downtimes.

  3. contracts that detail specific protections and maintenance services to be implemented.

  4. clear documentation for regular maintenance requirements, procedures, and logs to record such maintenance.

5. backup systems, such as an alternate equipment, power sources and off-line data storage.

6. documentation of disaster recovery protocols.

Chapter 10 – References

1. Greene, Adam H. "HIPAA Compliance for Clinician Texting" Journal of AHIMA 83, no.4 (April 2012): 34-36.

2. https://healthitsecurity.com/news/secure-texting-becoming-1st-choice-for-sending-healthcare-data

3. https://www.americanbar.org/groups/health_law/publications/aba_health_esource/2016-2017/september2017/texting information/

4. https://www.foxgrp.com/hipaa-compliance/hipaa-and-email-rules/

5. https://www.foxgrp.com/hipaa-compliance/hipaa-and-email-rules/

6. https://www.foxgrp.com/hipaa-compliance/hipaa-compliant-email/

7. Westgate, Aubrey. "Five Social Media Risks Medical Practices Should Watch Out For" Physicians Practice. (September 20, 2013). See http://www.physicianspractice.com/blog/five-social-media-risks-medical-practices-should-watch-out

8. Iafolla, Teresa. "11 Tips for Responding to Negative Patient Reviews Online," EVisit. (January 15, 2015). See https://evisit.com/tips-responding-negative-online-patient-reviews/.

9. Iafolla, Teresa. "11 Tips for Responding to Negative Patient Reviews Online," EVisit. (January 15, 2015). See https://evisit.com/tips-responding-negative-online-patient-reviews/.

10. Kepler, Tara and McGinty, Charlene. "Telemedicine: How to Assess Your Risks and Develop a Program that Works," presentation at the American Health Lawyers Association's Annual Hospitals and Health Systems Law Institute and Annual Physicians and Physician Organizations Institute, Phoenix, AZ (Feb. 10, 2009)

11. https://www.americanbar.org/groups/health_law/publications/aba_health_esource/2016-2017/september2017/texting information/

12. Maheu, Dr. Marlene. *Telehealth: RISK MANAGEMENT IN THE RE-TOOLING OF HEALTH CARE*; Behavioral Information Tomorrow Conference; March 18-21, 1999, San Jose, California.

Method of Participation for Obtaining CME Credit for Chapters 9 and 10

There are no fees to receive CME credit for participating in this activity. If you wish to receive continuing education credit, please do the following::

1. Review the objectives, statement of need, and disclosure information.

2. Read the indicated chapters.

3. To obtain the maximum benefit from this activity, you are encouraged to complete the self-assessment checklist at the end of each chapter, as applicable, and formulate an action plan based on each self-assessment exercise.

4. Go online using the URL below and complete the self-assessment (achieving a passing score of 70 percent) and the activity evaluation. If you do not achieve a passing score in three attempts, please contact CEServices@cme.com to have your account reset. Upon passing the assessment and completing the evaluation, you will be able to print or save your certificate of credit.

www.academycme.org/actID=19GU165
activity code: 19GU165

FREE CONSULTATION

Schedule a complimentary consultation with OJM Group to learn how the topics discussed in our books, articles and presentations may benefit you and your medical practice.

OJM Group has helped over 1,000 physicians:

- Reduce their income taxes.
- Shield practice and personal assets from lawsuits.
- Implement a more tax-efficient corporate structure.
- Utilize superior qualified and non-qualified benefit plans.
- Build investable wealth in a conservative, tax-savvy manner.
- Coordinate all areas of planning.

**Please visit www.ojmgroup.com
or call (877) 656-4362
to schedule your free consultation.**

ADDITIONAL RESOURCES FOR PHYSICIANS

These books for physicians are available in hard copy and ebook formats for Kindle and iPad. Please visit **www.ojmbookstore.com** and **use promotional code RMPP at checkout** to request or download your free book(s).

For Doctors Only: A Guide to Working & Building More teaches doctors the important lessons they never learned in medical school, residency or fellowship. Doctors learn how to efficiently leverage their time, money and effort so they can get more out of a medical practice. Specifically, doctors learn how to protect their personal and practice assets from lawsuits, taxes and bad investments as well as learning how they may build wealth and avoiding catastrophic financial disasters. *For Doctors Only* is a must have for any physician wishing to achieve financial success.

Wealth Protection Planning for Orthopaedic Surgeons and Sports Medicine Specialists Written by OJM principals and well-known orthopaedic surgeon Dr. Peter Millett of the Steadman Clinic in Vail, CO, this short book focuses on four concise lessons that may have a significant impact on your practice efficiency and long-term financial well-being. The book is structured in a Challenge-Solution format, featuring strategies for practice structure, tax and cost reduction, asset protection and building wealth.

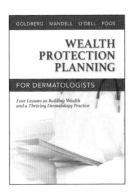

Wealth Protection Planning for Dermatologists Written by OJM principals and well-known dermatologist Dr. David Goldberg, this short book focuses on four concise lessons that may have a significant impact on a dermatologist's practice efficiency and long-term financial well-being. The book is structured in a Challenge-Solution format, featuring strategies for practice structure, tax and cost reduction, asset protection and building wealth.

SCHEDULE A SEMINAR

OJM Group's education experts have delivered seminars on asset protection, tax and estate planning for over 200 medical societies, associations, hospitals and other physician groups nationwide. OJM Group can provide this content in various formats including lectures, webcasts and pre-recorded videos.

REQUEST AUTHORS' ARTICLES FOR YOUR PUBLICATION

OJM Group partners and team members have authored more than a dozen books for physicians and written articles for over 100 periodicals, newsletters and websites. Article topics include asset protection, practice management, tax reduction, retirement planning, investing and estate planning.

OJM Group can provide this educational content to publications at no cost to the publisher, and will offer readers a free hard copy or ebook download of one of our books.

Please contact OJM Group at **877-656-4362** to schedule a seminar or request an article.

Visit **www.ojmgroup.com** to learn more about free educational materials and presentations for physicians.